2014-2015

HESI Live Review Workbook for the NCLEX-PN Exam

Rosemary Pine, PhD, RN, BC, CDE
Director, Review Courses
Elsevier Review and Testing
Nursing and Health Professions
Houston, Texas

Sandra L. Upchurch, PhD, RN
Director, Curriculum
Elsevier Review and Testing
Nursing and Health Professions
Houston, Texas

Traci Henry, MSN, RN
Curriculum Manager
Elsevier Review and Testing
Nursing and Health Professions
Houston, Texas

Marilyn Tompkins, DrPH, RN, FNP, BC
Family Nurse Practitioner
Lakeside-Milam Recovery Centers
Kirkland, Washington

Judy Siefert, MSN, RN
Director, Testing
Elsevier Review and Testing
Nursing and Health Professions
Houston, Texas

Cathy Griteman, MSN, RN
Testing Manager
Elsevier Review and Testing
Nursing and Health Professions
Houston, Texas

Editors

Rosemary Pine, PhD, RN, BC, CDE
Director, Review Courses
Elsevier Review and Testing
Nursing and Health Professions
Houston, Texas

Ashley Mezger, MA
Associate e-Project Manager
Elsevier Review and Testing
Nursing and Health Professions
Houston, Texas

The editors and publisher would also like to acknowledge the following individuals for contributions to the previous editions of this book.

Susan Morrison, PhD, RN, FAAN
President Emerita
Elsevier Review and Testing
Nursing and Health Professions
Houston, Texas

Ainslie Nibert, PhD, RN, FAAN
Vice President
Elsevier Review and Testing
Nursing and Health Professions
Houston, Texas

Mickie Hinds, PhD, RN
Former Director, Review and Curriculum
Elsevier Review and Testing
Nursing and Health Professions
Houston, Texas

Denise Voyles, BSN, RN
Testing Manager
Elsevier Review and Testing
Nursing and Health Professions
Houston, Texas

D1299711

ELSEVIER

3251 Riverport Lane
St. Louis, MO 63043

2014-2015 HESI Live
Review Workbook for the NCLEX-PN Exam

ISBN: 978-1-4557-5113-6

NOTICE

Knowledge and best practice in the field of practical nursing are constantly changing. As new research and experience broaden our understanding, changes in research methods, professional practices, or medical treatment may become necessary.

Practitioners and researchers must always rely on their own experience and knowledge in evaluating and using any information, methods, compounds, or experiments described herein. In using such information or methods, they should be mindful of their own safety and the safety of others, including parties for whom they have a professional responsibility.

With respect to any drug or pharmaceutical products identified, readers are advised to check the most current information provided (i) on procedures featured or (ii) by the manufacturer of each product to be administered, to verify the recommended dose or formula, the method and duration of administration, and contraindications. It is the responsibility of practitioners, relying on their own experience and knowledge of their clients, to make diagnoses, to determine dosages and the best treatment for each individual client, and to take all appropriate safety precautions.

To the fullest extent of the law, neither the Publisher nor the authors, contributors, or editors assume any liability for any injury and/or damage to persons or property as a matter of products liability, negligence, or otherwise, or from any use or operation of any methods, products, instructions, or ideas contained in the material herein.

The Publisher

NCLEX®, NCLEX-RN®, and NCLEX-PN® are registered trademarks of the National Council of State Boards of Nursing, Inc.

NANDA International Nursing Diagnoses: Definitions and Classifications 2012-2014; Herdman T.H. (ED); copyright © 2012, 1994-2012 NANDA International; published by John Wiley & Sons, Limited.

International Standard Book Number: 978-1-4557-5113-6

Executive Content Strategist: Kristin Geen
Associate Content Development Specialist: Laura Goodrich
Publishing Services Manager: Jeff Patterson
Senior Project Manager: Anne Konopka
Designer: Karen Pauls

Printed in the United States of America

Last digit is the print number: 9 8 7 6 5 4 3 2 1

Working together
to grow libraries in
developing countries

www.elsevier.com • www.bookaid.org

1 Test-Taking Strategies and Study Guide

Welcome to the Hesi Live Review Course

This series of slides and the workbook provide test-taking strategies, sample test questions, and a content review of the nursing curriculum to help prepare nursing students for the NCLEX-PN examination. For a more in-depth review of certain material, please refer to the following:

- *HESI Comprehensive Review for the NCLEX-PN Examination*
- *Mosby's Comprehensive Review of Nursing for NCLEX-PN Examination*
- *Saunders Comprehensive Review for the NCLEX-PN Examination*

Knowledge is power!

Goals of the Live Review Course
- Strengthen test-taking skills
- Provide practice answering NCLEX style questions
- Incorporate recommended strategies to manage anxiety
- Formulate a study plan using tools such as the HESI Live Review Workbook for the NCLEX-PN Exam
- Review basic curriculum content

NLCEX-PN Examination

About the NCLEX-PN Blueprint
The test plan is revised every 3 years after a practice analysis has been conducted with entry-level nurses.

Information about the test plan, including descriptions of content categories and related content for each category, can be found on the website for the National Council of State Boards of Nursing *(www.ncsbn.org)*.

The NCSBN website also presents information for students, frequently asked questions, and examples of alternate formats.

The content of the NCLEX-PN Test Plan covers essential nursing knowledge in four client needs categories, as shown in the following section.

Client Needs Categories
- Safe and Effective Care Environment
  — Coordinated Care
  — Safety and Infection Control
- Health Promotion and Maintenance
- Psychosocial Integrity
- Physiological Integrity
  — Basic Care and Comfort
  — Pharmacological Therapies
  — Reduction of Risk Potential
  — Physiological Adaptation

1

Processes

Processes fundamental to PN practice are integrated into all client needs categories.

- Nursing process
  - Planning and implementing nursing care based on assessment, diagnosis, and determining priorities
  - Evaluating the effectiveness of nursing care
- Caring
- Communication and documentation
- Teaching and learning

About Test Administration

With computerized adaptive testing (CAT), the difficulty of the exam is tailored to the candidate's ability level.

All practical/vocational nurse candidates must answer a minimum of 85 items. The maximum number of items the candidate may answer during the allotted 5-hour period is 205.

About Test Item Questions

Multiple choice items

- Majority of items
- One question with four choices (answers) from which to choose the correct response

Multiple response items

- Require the candidate to select one or more than one response from five to seven choices
- The item instructs the candidate to choose all that apply

Fill-in-the-blank items

- Require a candidate to type one or more numbers in a blank after a calculation is completed
- If rounding is necessary, it is performed at the end of the calculation

Hot spot items

- Instructs the candidate to identify one or more areas on a picture or graphic
- Can measure knowledge related to safety, physical assessment, and other skills

Chart/exhibit format

- Presents the candidate with a problem that requires the individual to review the information in the chart/exhibit to arrive at the answer
- Provides the client history, laboratory data, and clinical data on tabs

Ordered response items or drag and drop

- Require a candidate to rank order or move options to provide the correct answer
- Presents the candidate with a list of the essential steps of a nursing procedure (e.g., CPR) and instructs the individual to order the steps in the correct sequence

Audio item format

- Presents the candidate with an audio clip; the individual with the aid of headphones then uses headphones to listen to the clip and selects the answer that applies.
- Evaluates the candidate's competence in certain skills or assessment areas.

Graphic options

- May be used as all or part of an individual item, either in the question itself or as part of the response.

Test-Taking Strategies

General Strategies

- Every question must be answered to move to the next question, so make your best guess if you are not sure of the answer.
- Quickly eliminate choices that do not answer the question.
- Reread the question for qualifiers or other words that specify what the question asks.
- Decide what makes the responses different from each other.
- Keep in mind that the choice may contain correct information but may not answer the question.

For Your Toolbox

- Use the *ABC*s when selecting an answer or determining the order of priority.
  - Remember the order of priority: airway, breathing, and circulation.
  - The exception to the rule is when using CPR, C-A-B is the order of priority.
- *Maslow's Hierarchy of Needs*
  - Address physiological needs first, followed by safety and security needs, love and belonging needs, self-esteem needs, and self-actualization needs.
  - When a physiological need is not addressed in the question, look for the option that addresses safety.
- Carefully read the question to determine the step of the nursing process.
  - *Data collection* questions involve the gathering of data.
  - *Planning* questions require collaboration and assisting with the development of a plan of care.
  - *Implementation* questions address issues of assisting with organizing and managing care and communicating nursing interventions thoroughly and accurately.
  - *Evaluation* questions focus on comparing the actual outcomes of care with the expected outcomes and on communicating and documenting findings.
- Think: safety, safety, SAFETY!
- Collect data before taking action, when appropriate.
- Have all necessary information and take all possible relevant actions before calling the physician/healthcare provider.

- Start with the least invasive intervention.
- Determine which client to assess first (i.e., most at risk, most physiologically unstable).
- Follow guidelines for delegating assignments. Remember the differences between the role of the licensed nurse and the role of the unlicensed assistive personnel (UAP).

The Question May Contain "Red Flag" Words

Practice rewording the following questions:
1. "Which response indicates to the nurse a need to reteach the client about …"
2. "Which prescription (order) should the nurse question?"

Common Interventions

- Small, frequent feedings
- Alternate rest with activity
- Conserve energy with any activity

Teaching Points

- Risk factors—known modifiable versus nonmodifiable
- Prevention and wellness promotion
- New medications/self-care instructions
- Client empowerment
- Anticipatory guidance
- Incorporating client education information into the client's lifestyle, culture, spiritual beliefs, and so on

A Few Words About "Words"

Healthcare provider (HCP): The person prescribing care (e.g., physician, nurse practitioner)

Prescriptions: Orders written by licensed healthcare providers

Unlicensed assistive personnel (UAP)

- Client care technician
- Nursing assistant
- Nurse's aide

Keep Memorizing to a Minimum

- Growth and developmental milestones
- Death and dying stages
- Crisis intervention
- Immunizations
- Drug classifications
- Principles of teaching/learning
- Stages of pregnancy and fetal growth
- Nurse Practice Act: Standards of Practice and delegation

Specific Strategies for Success in Answering NCLEX-PN Questions—Four Essential Steps

1. Determine whether the style of the question is
   + positive +
   or
   – negative –
2. Find the key words in the question.
3. Rephrase the question in your own words and then answer the question.
4. Rule out options.

Practice Rewording

1. _____
2. _____

Determine Whether the Question Is Written in a Positive or Negative Style

- A *positive style* may ask what the nurse should do, or the best or first action to implement.
- A *negative style* may ask what the nurse should avoid, which prescription the nurse should question, or which behavior indicates the need for reteaching the client.

Find the Key Words in the Question

- Ask yourself which words or phrases provide the critical information.
- This information may be the age of the client, the setting, the timing, a set of symptoms or behaviors, or any number of other factors.
- For example, the nursing actions for a 10-year-old, 1-day postoperative client are different from those for a 70-year-old, 1-hour postoperative client.

Rephrase the Question in Your Own Words and Answer the Question

- This will help you to eliminate nonessential information in the question and to determine the correct answer.
- Ask yourself, "What is this instructor *really* asking?"
- Before looking at the choices, rephrase the question in your own words.
- Answer the question.

Rule Out Options

- Based on your knowledge, you can probably identify one or two options that are clearly incorrect.
- Mentally mark through those options on the computer monitor.
- Now, differentiate between the remaining options, considering your knowledge of the subject and related nursing principles, such as the roles of the nurse, the nursing process, the ABCs, and Maslow's Hierarchy of Needs.

A client in a skilled nursing facility reports to the PN that he has not had a bowel movement in 2 days. Which intervention should the PN implement first?

A. Instruct the UAP to offer a glass of warm prune juice at mealtimes.

B. Ask the charge nurse to request a prescription for a stool softener.

C. Assess the client's medical record to determine his normal bowel pattern.

D. Instruct a family member to offer the client fluids, up to five 8-ounce glasses a day.

HESI Test Question Approach			
Positive?		YES	NO
Key Words			
Rephrase			
Rule Out Choices			
A	B	C	D

A client who has COPD is resting in a semi-Fowler's position with oxygen at 2 L/min per nasal cannula. The client develops dyspnea. What action should the PN implement first?

A. Call the healthcare provider.
B. Obtain a bedside pulse oximeter.
C. Raise the head of the bed further.
D. Assess the client's vital signs.

HESI Test Question Approach

Positive?		YES	NO
Key Words			
Rephrase			
Rule Out Choices			
A	B	C	D

Specific Areas of Content

Laboratory Values

Know the normal ranges for commonly used laboratory tests, what variations mean, and the *best* nursing actions.

- H & H
- WBC, RBC, platelets
- Electrolytes: K^+, Na^+, Ca^{2+}, Mg^{2+}, Cl^-, PO_4
- BUN and creatinine
- *Relationship* of Ca^{2+} and PO_4
- ABGs
- PT, INR, PTT (don't get them confused)

A client who has hyperparathyroidism is scheduled to receive a prescribed dose of oral phosphate. The PN notes that the client's serum calcium level is 12.5 mg/dL. What action should the nurse implement?

A. Hold the phosphate and notify the healthcare provider.
B. Review the client's serum parathyroid hormone level.
C. Give a PRN dose of IV calcium per protocol.
D. Administer the dose of oral phosphate.

HESI Test Question Approach

Positive?		YES	NO
Key Words			
Rephrase			
Rule Out Choices			
A	B	C	D

In completing a client's preoperative routine, the PN finds that the operative permit has not been signed. The client begins to ask more questions about the surgical procedure. What action should the nurse take next?

A. Witness the client's signature on the permit.
B. Answer the client's questions about the surgery.
C. Inform the charge nurse that the client has questions about the surgery.
D. Reassure the client that the surgeon will answer any questions before the anesthesia is administered.

HESI Test Question Approach

Positive?		YES	NO
Key Words			
Rephrase			
Rule Out Choices			
A	B	C	D

Nutrition

- Be able to identify foods relative to their sodium content (high or low), potassium level (high or low), and increased levels of phosphate, iron, or vitamin K.
- Chemotherapy, GI/GU disturbances
- Proteins, CHOs, fats
- Pregnancy and fetal growth needs
- Remember the following concepts:
  — Introducing one food at a time (infants, allergies)
  — Progression "AS TOLERATED"
    - What nursing assessment guides decisions about progression?

Medication Administration and Pharmacology

Pharmacological treatment and related nursing implications are reviewed in each chapter to coincide with the disease processes and conditions of the client.

More critical thinking questions are being designed around SKILLS!

Think: safety, safety, SAFETY!

Reflect on … the *whole picture.*

Safe medication administration is more than just knowing the action of the medications. It also includes:
- The "6 Rights" (six *plus* technique of skill execution)
  — Right drug
  — Right dose
  — Right route
  — Right time
  — Right patient
  — Right documentation
- Drug interactions
- Vulnerable organs (√ labs; what to assess)
- Allergies and presence of suprainfections
- Concept of peak and trough

How you would know:
- Whether the drug is working
- A problem has arisen

Teaching: *safety, empowerment, compliance*

Practical Tips

Do not respond to the NCLEX question based on your personal experiences …
- *Your* past client care experiences or agency
- A familiar phrase or term
- "Of course, *I* would have already …"
- What *you* think is *realistic*
- *Your* children, pregnancies, parents, elders, personal response to a drug, and so on

Do respond based on …
- ABCs
- Scientific, behavioral, sociological principles
- Principles of teaching/learning
- Maslow's Hierarchy of Needs
- Nursing process

- What the question asks: no more, no less
- NCLEX-PN ideal hospital
- Basic A & P
- Critical thinking

Best Practice for a Successful NCLEX-PN Exam

Manage Anxiety Between Now and the Test
- Think positively and believe in yourself.
- Use positive self-talk ("I can do this!")
- Set up a study schedule and stick to it.
- Avoid negative people.
- Respect your body and your mind.
- Establish a balanced lifestyle (i.e., a regular schedule for sleeping, eating, exercising, socializing, and working).

Develop a Study Schedule
- Organize resources.
  - Online texts, hard copy books, review questions
  - Practice tests, case studies
- Identify your strengths and challenges; review these:
  - Results of your HESI Exit Exam
  - Final grades
  - Feedback on clinical performance
  - Results of practice tests
  - Your personal identification of your strengths and weakness of content during this LRC
- Initially take practice tests specific to your areas of weakness.
- Establish a study schedule that includes adequate time to prepare.
- Know your testing date.
  - Plan your schedule for the 4 to 8 weeks before your testing date.
- Would a study group help you?
- Make sure you have a comfortable level of understanding of growth and development markers, labs, drug categories, drug calculations, and immunization schedules.

A Week before the Exam
- Take a test drive to the site.
- Be mindful of traffic patterns.
- Familiarize yourself with the test center.
- Confirm that you have all the documents you need to be admitted to the exam.

The Day Before the Test
- *Do* allow only 30 minutes to review test-taking strategies.
- If you feel the need to review your notes the night before the exam, do so, but allow for a restful 7 to 8 hours of sleep.

- *Do* assemble all necessary materials:
  — Admission ticket
  — Directions to testing center
  — Identification
  — Money for lunch
- *Do* something you enjoy.
- *Do* respect your body and your mind.

The Day of the Test
- Eat a healthy meal.
- *Do* allow plenty of time to get to the testing center.
- *Do* dress comfortably.
- *Do* take *only* your identification forms into the testing room.
- *Do* avoid distractions.
- *Do* use positive self-talk.

At the Exam
- Breathe deeply and regularly.
- Continue the positive self-talk.
- Be in the moment and take the exam; no regrets.
- Do not allow the number of questions to influence your level of self-confidence.

You can do this!

2 Legal Aspects of Care and the Leadership Role of the Practical Nurse

Legal Aspects

Legal Systems

- Civil law is concerned with the protection of the client's private rights.
- Criminal law deals with the rights of individuals and society as defined by legislative laws.

Nursing negligence is the failure to exercise the proper degree of care required by the circumstances that a reasonably prudent person would exercise under the circumstances to avoid harming others. It is a careless act of omission or commission that results in injury to another.

Nursing malpractice, often referred to as *professional negligence,* is a type of negligence. It is the failure to use the degree of care that a reasonable nurse would use under the same or similar circumstances.

Malpractice is found when:
- The nurse owed a duty to the client.
- The nurse did not carry out that duty or breached that duty.
- The client was injured.
- The nurse's failure to carry out that duty caused the client's injury.

Standards of Care

- Nurses are required to follow standards of care, which originate in Nurse Practice Acts, the guidelines of professional organizations.
- Nurses are required to follow written policies and procedures of their employing institutions.
- Nurses are responsible for performing procedures correctly and exercising professional judgment when implementing healthcare provider's prescriptions.

A UAP (unlicensed assistive personnel) is transporting a client with newly developed pulselessness of the right leg for an angiogram. In the elevator the UAP overhears two nurses talking about a client who will lose her leg because of the negligence of the staff. What federal law is violated?
A. Health Insurance Portability and Accountability Act (HIPAA)
B. Americans with Disabilities Act (ADA)
C. Nurse Practice Act (NPA)
D. Patient Self-Determination Act (PSDA)

HESI Test Question Approach			
Positive?		YES	NO
Key Words			
Rephrase			
Rule Out Choices			
A	B	C	D

Practice Issues

- Nurses must follow the healthcare provider's prescription unless the nurse believes that it is in error; that it violates hospital policy; or that it is harmful to the client.
- If the healthcare provider confirms the prescription and the LVN/LPN still believes the order is inappropriate, the nurse should contact the supervisor to intervene.
- The nurse makes a formal report explaining the refusal.
- The nurse should file an incident report (variance or occurrence) for any situation in which harm to the client may have resulted.

Advance Directives

- Assess the client's knowledge of advance directives.
- Integrate them into the client's plan of care.
- Provide the client with information about advance directives.
- Advance directives can limit life-prolonging measures when there is little or no chance of recovery.
  — Living will—A client documents his or her wishes regarding future care in the event of terminal illness.
  — Durable power of attorney for healthcare—A client appoints a representative (healthcare proxy) to make healthcare decisions.

Informed Consent

- It is the duty of the physician or nurse practitioner who is performing the procedure or treatment to obtain informed consent.
- The PN is witnessing the signature, not providing informed consent.
- Answers to any questions the client has about a procedure are the responsibility of the healthcare provider who will perform the procedure.

Abuse

- The National Center on Elder Abuse identifies the two most important indicators of abuse as (1) frequent, unexplained crying by the elderly individual, and (2) an older person's unexplained fear or suspicion of a particular person or people in the home.
- The nurse has legal responsibilities with regard to reporting incidences of abuse, neglect, or violence.
- Healthcare professionals who do not report suspected abuse or neglect are liable for civil or criminal legal action.

Restraints/Safety Reminder Devices (SRDs)

- Restraints and SRDs are used to ensure the physical safety of the client or of other clients when less restrictive interventions are unsuccessful. They are used only on the written prescription of a healthcare provider.
- The nurse must follow agency policy and procedure to restrain any client.
- Documentation of the use of restraints and of follow-up assessments must detail the attempts to use less restrictive interventions.

A family member of a female client who is in a Posey vest restraint (SRD) asks why the restraint was applied. How should the practical nurse respond?

A. The restraint was prescribed by the healthcare provider.
B. There are not enough staff members to keep the client safe all the time.
C. The other clients are upset when the client wanders at night.
D. The client's actions place her at high risk for harming herself.

HESI Test Question Approach

Positive?   YES   NO

Key Words *Safety*

Rephrase

Rule Out Choices

A   B   C   D

Legal Aspects of Mental Health Nursing

- Admissions
  — Involuntary
  — Emergency
- Client's rights
- Competency

What nursing action has the highest priority when admitting a client to a psychiatric unit on an involuntary basis?

A. Reassure the client that the admission is only for a limited time.
B. Offer the client and family the opportunity to share their feelings about the admission.
C. Determine the behaviors that resulted in the need for admission.
D. Advise the client about the legal rights of all hospitalized clients.

HESI Test Question Approach

Positive?   YES   NO

Key Words *Involuntary*

Rephrase *Why are they there?*

Rule Out Choices

A   B   C   D

Confidential Health Care

- All clients are protected under the Health Insurance Portability and Accountability Act of 1996 (HIPAA).
  — HIPAA sets standards for the verbal, written and electronic exchange of private health information.
  — HIPAA establishes the client's rights to consent to the use and disclosure of health information; to inspect and copy his or her medical record; and to amend mistaken or incomplete information.

Good Samaritan Laws

- These laws protect from liability those who give first aid in an emergency situation.
- The LPN/LVN must only provide reasonable and prudent care that is consistent with his or her level of expertise.

12

Leadership Role of the Practical Nurse

Communication Skills
Consider the type of leadership indicated by these verbal examples:

"Do it my way."

- Aggressive communication/authoritarian leader

"Whatever ... as long as you like me."

- Passive communication/laissez-faire leader

"Let's consider the options available."

- Assertive communication/democratic leader

Delegation
- The process by which responsibility and authority, *but not accountability,* are transferred to another individual.
- Neither the nursing process nor any activity requiring nursing judgment may be delegated to a UAP.
- Five rights of delegation
  — Right task
  — Right circumstance
  — Right person
  — Right direction/communication
  — Right supervision

Which assignment should the PN delegate to a UAP in a long-term acute care setting? (Select all that apply.)
A. Checking the blood glucose level before meals for a client with an insulin order.
B. Giving PO medications left at the bedside for the client to take after eating.
C. Taking vital signs for an older client with left humerus and left tibial fractures.
D. Replacing an abdominal dressing that has been soiled by incontinence.
E. Obtaining a culture and sensitivity sample from a central line catheter site.

Handoff Communication
A communication in which important client information is shared at pertinent points of care (e.g., change of shift, transfer from one clinical setting to another).
- Ensures continuity of care and client safety.
- Improves communication and appropriate delegation.

HESI Test Question Approach		
Positive?	YES	NO
Key Words Delegate to UAP		
Rephrase		
Rule Out Choices		
A	B	C	D

A nurse is preparing for change of shift. Which action by the nurse is characteristic of an ineffective handoff communication?
A. The PN tells the nurse coming on duty that a client is anxious about his pain, and needs to have information about the use of an incentive spirometer reinforced.
B. The nurse refers to the electronic medical record (EMR) to review the client's medication administration record.
C. During rounds the nurse talks about the problem the UAP created by not performing a fingerstick blood glucose test on the client.
D. Before giving report, the nurse performs rounds on her assigned clients so that there is less likelihood of interruption during handoff.

S-BAR

S-BAR is an interdisciplinary communication strategy that promotes effective communication between caregivers.

S SITUATION—State the issue or problem.
B BACKGROUND—Provide the client's history.
A ASSESSMENT—Give the most recent vital signs and current findings.
R RECOMMENDATION—State what should be done.

The PN has UAPs on the team. Which client task or tasks could be assigned a UAP? (Select all that apply.)
A. Transporting a client scheduled for a STAT CT scan.
B. Bathing a client receiving IV Vancomycin (Vancocin) through a peripherally inserted central catheter (PICC) line.
C. Removing a Foley catheter, per the healthcare provider's prescription, and encouraging voiding in 8 hours.
D. Reconnecting the prescribed negative pressure vacuum (Wound VAC) to a client with a pressure ulcer.
E. Clearing the alarm on the IV pump and restarting the pump.

The PN is making assignments for five clients at the nursing home. The nursing team includes a licensed practical nurse (LPN), and two UAPs. Which client task or tasks would be assigned to the UAPs? (Select all that apply.)
A. Administering an injection of enoxaparin sodium (Lovenox) to a client who requires anticoagulant therapy.
B. Repositioning a client with a stage 3 pressure ulcer who needs a bed bath.
C. Checking the residual for a client with an enteral feeding absorbing at 30 mL/hour.
D. Changing the IV tubing on a client recovering from pneumonia.
E. Performing a straight catheterization on a client prescribed intermittent catheterization.

HESI Test Question Approach			
Positive?		YES	NO
Key Words	*which action*		
Rephrase			
Rule Out Choices			
A	B	C	D

HESI Test Question Approach			
Positive?		YES	NO
Key Words	*Assigned to UAPs*		
Rephrase			
Rule Out Choices			
A	B	C	D

HESI Test Question Approach			
Positive?		YES	NO
Key Words	*Assigned to UAPs*		
Rephrase			
Rule Out Choices			
A	B	C	D

Which situation warrants a variance (incident) report by the nurse?

A. Refusal by a client to take prescribed medication
B. Improved client status before completion of the course of medication
C. An allergic reaction by the client to a prescribed medication
D. A client received medication prescribed for another client.

HESI Test Question Approach			
Positive?		~~YES~~	NO
Key Words	Incident report		
Rephrase			
Rule Out Choices			
~~A~~	~~B~~	~~C~~	D

Chapter **2** **Legal Aspects of Care and the Leadership Role of the Practical Nurse**

3 Clinical Concepts and Mechanisms of Disease for the Practical Nurse

[Handwritten notes, top right]
Precipitating factors → History of pain
Onset
Location
Duration
Characteristics
Aggravating factors
Relieving factors
Time
Severity → Pain scale

Pain

- Pain is whatever the client says it is.
- Pain is the fifth vital sign.
- Pain occurs in all clinical settings.
- Nurses have a central role in pain assessment and management.
  — Communicating with other healthcare providers
  — Ensuring the initiation and coordination of adequate pain relief measures
  — Evaluating the effectiveness of interventions
  — Advocating for clients with pain
- Pain medications generally are divided into three categories:
  — Nonopioids—mild pain
  — Opioids—moderate to severe pain
  — Co-analgesic or adjuvant drugs—neuropathic pain

Types of Pain Medications
Nonopioid Analgesics

- Acetaminophen (Tylenol)
  — Maximum recommended dosage is 4,000 mg (4 g) in 24 hours
  — Monitor liver function
- Salicylates
  — Aspirin
  — Choline magnesium trisalicylate (Trilisate)
- Nonsteroidal antiinflammatory drugs (NSAIDs)
  — Ibuprofen (Motrin, Nuprin, Advil)
  — Indomethacin (Indocin)
  — Ketorolac (Toradol)
  — Diclofenac K (Cataflam)
  — Cyclooxygenase-2 (COX-2) inhibitor
  — Celecoxib (Celebrex)

[Handwritten note] ← know the classes

Opioid Analgesics

- Mu agonists
  — Morphine (Roxanol, MS Contin, Avinza, Kadian, Epimorph, MSIR, Oramorph SR)
  — Hydromorphone (Dilaudid)
  — Methadone (Dolophine)
  — Levorphanol (Levo-Dromoran)
  — Fentanyl (Sublimaze, Duragesic, Actiq)
  — Oxycodone (Percocet, Percodan, Endocet, Tylox, Roxicodone, OxyContin, Combunox)
  — Hydrocodone (Lortab, Vicodin, Zydone)
  — Codeine (Tylenol No. 3)
- Mixed opioid agonist-antagonists
  — Pentazocine (Talwin)
  — Butorphanol (Stadol)
  — Buprenorphine (Buprenex)
  — Buprenorphine plus naloxone (Suboxone)

- Adjuvant drugs
  — Used for neuropathic pain
  — Antiepileptic drugs, antidepressants, and anesthetics are prescribed alone or in combination with opioids for neuropathic pain
  — Corticosteroids

Nonpharmacologic Pain Relief Techniques

- Noninvasive
  — Heat and cold application
  — Massage therapy
  — Relaxation techniques
  — Guided imagery
  — Biofeedback techniques
- Invasive
  — Nerve blocks
  — Interruption of neural pathways
  — Acupuncture

Fluids and Electrolytes

Fluid Volume Excess

- Causes
  — CHF (most common), renal failure, cirrhosis, overhydration
- Symptoms
  — Peripheral edema, periorbital edema, elevated BP, dyspnea, altered LOC
- Lab findings
  — $\downarrow$ BUN, $\downarrow$ Hgb, $\downarrow$ Hct, $\downarrow$ serum osmolality, $\downarrow$ urine specific gravity
- Treatment
  — Diuretics, fluid restriction, weigh daily, monitor K^+

Fluid Volume Deficit

- Causes
  — Inadequate fluid intake, hemorrhage, vomiting, diarrhea, massive edema
- Symptoms
  — Weight loss, oliguria, postural hypotension
- Lab findings
  — $\uparrow$ BUN and creatinine may be elevated or normal, < Hgb, $\uparrow$ Hct, $\uparrow$ urine specific gravity
- Treatment
  — Strict I & O, replace with isotonic fluids, monitor BP, weigh daily

Electrolyte Imbalances

Hyponatremia

- Na^+ < 135 mEq/L
- Muscle cramps, confusion
- Check BP frequently
- Restrict fluids, cautious IV replacement as needed

Excess

CHF
Left → lungs (dyspnea, crackles, productive lungs) drowning
Right → Edema, jugular vein distention
Both → BP increased

Excess volume = Excess ICP = Altered LOC
for pitting edema, every +1 = 2mm

Deficit

oliguria = decreased urination
BUN + creatinine is elevated
monitor BP for signs of shock

give normal saline = isotonic
or hypertonic (0.33-0.55) saline solutions

isotonic = "I so perfect" 0.9% solution
hypertonic = "hyper" dehydrate 3-5%
hypo = "hippo" swell of cell - plump 0.33-0.55 %
*know hyper-, hypo-, and isotonic solutions

—sodium

q/L

ema, seizures, thirst, fever
ontain sodium
- Restrict sodium in diet
- Weigh daily

Hypokalemia
- $K^+ < 3.5$ mEq/L
- Rapid, thready pulse, flat T waves, fatigue, anorexia, muscle cramps
- IV potassium supplements
- Encourage foods high in K+ (bananas, oranges, spinach)

Hyperkalemia
- $K^+ > 5$ mEq/L
- Tall, tented T waves, bradycardia, muscle weakness
- 10% to 20% glucose with regular insulin
- Kayexalate – *strong laxative*
- Renal dialysis may be required

"calcium" - helps muscles contract

Hypocalcemia
- $Ca^{2+} < 8.5$ mEq/L
- + Trousseau's sign, + Chvostek's sign, diarrhea, numbness, convulsions
- Administer calcium supplements
- IV calcium (give slowly)
- Increase dietary calcium

Hypercalcemia
- $Ca^{2+} > 10.5$ mEq/L
- Muscle weakness, constipation, nausea and vomiting (N/V), dysrhythmias, behavioral changes
- Limit vitamin D intake
- Avoid calcium-based antacids
- Calcitonin to reduce calcium
- Renal dialysis may be required

Acid Base

The basics for interpreting ABG results are as follows:
- pH
  — Normal = 7.35-7.45
  — <7.35 = acidosis
  — >7.45 = alkalosis
- P_{CO_2}
  — Normal = 35-45 mm Hg
  — >45 = acidosis
  — <35 = alkalosis
- HCO_3
  — Normal = 22 to 26 mEq/L
  — <22 = acidosis
  — >26 = alkalosis

Handwritten notes:

Outside of cell — Sodium + Chloride
Inside of cell —

diuretics common cause of hypo. unless taking Potassium-sparing diuretic

hyper → most EKG changes

Trousseau's = "down to trousers"
Chvostek = twitch in cheek

hyper = related specifically to cancer

Arterial Blood Gas Interpretation Practice

1. Determine whether the pH value is normal, acidotic, or alkalotic.
   - A. 7.31 **acidotic**
   - B. 7.47 **alkalotic**
   - C. 7.36 **normal**

2. Determine whether the client is hypoventilating, hyperventilating, or has normal ventilation.
   - A. P_{CO_2} = 42 **normal**
   - B. P_{CO_2} = 33 **hyperventilating**
   - C. P_{CO_2} = 55 **hypoventilating**

3. Determine whether the client is retaining or eliminating bicarbonate.
   - A. HCO_3 = 20 **eliminating**
   - B. HCO_3 = 33 **retaining**
   - C. HCO_3 = 21 **eliminating**

The PN is reviewing the electronic medical records of the assigned clients. Which is/are at high risk for a potassium deficit? (Select all that apply.)
A. The client with hyperthyroidism
B. The client with metabolic acidosis   • **diuretics**
C. The client with intestinal obstruction   • **vomiting**
D. The client receiving nasogastric suction
E. The client with watery diarrhea

pH	7.35	Normal	7.45
CO_2	55		35
HCO_3	22		26

HESI Test Question Approach

Positive?		YES	NO
Key Words	**Potassium deficit**		
Rephrase			
Rule Out Choices			
A	B	C	D

alkalosis

| Safety

Falls
- Sentinel event
- Adult risk factors—stroke, depression, mobility issue, history of seizure, history of falls, use of assistive devices, polypharmacy, environmental issues, forgetting or ignoring mobility issues
- Pediatric risk factors—length of stay, IV or saline lock, use of antiseizure medications, acute or chronic orthopedic diagnosis, receiving physical or occupational therapy, history of falling. Consider age, stage of growth and development, too.

Nursing and Collaborative Management
- Fall prevention
  — Safety surveillance
  — Assess need for pain relief, toileting, positioning
  — Frequent reorientation
- Client and family education
- Address environmental concerns
- Sitter

High-Alert Medications

- These are the drugs most likely to cause significant harm to the client even when used as intended.
- Anticoagulants, narcotics and opiates, insulin, chemotherapeutic drugs, and sedatives are the most common high-alert medications.
- The most common types of harm associated with these medications are hypotension, bleeding, hypoglycemia, delirium, lethargy, and bradycardia.
- Strategies to prevent harm
  — Built-in redundancies
  — Double-checking
  — Smart pumps
  — Standardized or protocol order sets

opiates = vasodialator = BP drop
diuretics = fluid deficit = BP drop

An intravenous prescription specifies 3,000 mL of 5% dextrose (D_5W) to run over a 24-hour period. The drop factor is 10 gtt/mL. There is 300 mL remaining at 0900. What time should the PN anticipate the next bag of D_5W solution to be hung? (Fill in the blank.)
The next bag of D_5W solution will be hung at _____ _____.

Death and Grief

- Stages of grief
  — Denial
  — Anger
  — Bargaining
  — Depression
  — Acceptance
- Encourage the client to express emotions.
- Do not take away the defense mechanism or coping mechanism the client uses in a crisis.
- Customs surrounding death and dying vary among cultures. Make every attempt to understand and accommodate the family's cultural traditions when caring for a dying client.

Infection and HIV

Infection

- Invasion of the body by a pathogen
- Response to the invasion
  — Localized   *＊Immunocompromised*
  — Systemic
- Nosocomial infections
  — Acquired as a result of exposure to a microorganism in a hospital setting

HIV
Routes of Transmission

- Unprotected sexual contact
- Exposure to blood through drug-use equipment
- Perinatal transmission
- Can occur during pregnancy, at the time of delivery, or after birth through breast-feeding

NCLEX still says mother-baby transmission is high risk.

Symptoms
- May show flulike symptoms in the earliest stage and advance to:
  — Severe weight loss
  — Secondary infections
  — Cancers
  — Neurologic disease

Diagnosis
- Enzyme-linked immunosorbent assay (ELISA) is usually done first (shown to have 99% reliability).
- The Western blot test is used as a confirmation test (shown to have 99.99% reliability).
- Clients who test negative initially should be retested in 3 to 6 months because of the lag time between exposure and a positive test result.
- Polymerase chain reaction (PCR) used with neonates.
- OraQuick In-Home HIV Test—A positive result is only preliminary; it must be confirmed by a healthcare professional.

HIV Drug Therapy
The goals of drug therapy are to:
- Reduce the viral load
- Maintain or raise the CD4+ T-cell counts *"fighter cells"*
- Delay the development of HIV-related symptoms and opportunistic diseases

Side Effects
Multiple drug interactions are possible between nucleoside reverse transcriptase inhibitors (NRTIs) and other drugs.

HIV Medications
- Nucleoside reverse transcriptase inhibitors (NRTIs)
  — Zidovudine (AZT, ZDV, Retrovir)
  — Lamivudine (3TC, Epivir)
  — Abacavir (Ziagen)
  — Emtricitabine (FTC, Emtriva)
- Nucleotide reverse transcriptase inhibitor (NtRTI)
  — Tenofovir DF (Viread)
- Non-nucleoside reverse transcriptase inhibitors (NNRTIs) NNRTIs are able to convert into enzymes that inhibit viral replication. A serious, harmful side effect is hepatotoxicity.
  — Nevirapine (Viramune)
  — Delavirdine (Rescriptor)
  — Efavirenz (Sustiva)
- Protease inhibitors (PIs)
  — Indinavir (Crixivan)
  — Ritonavir (Norvir)
  — Nelfinavir (Viracept)
  — Amprenavir (Agenerase)
  — Atazanavir (Reyataz)
  — Fosamprenavir (Lexiva)
  — Tipranavir (Aptivus)
  — Darunavir (Prezista)

HIV meds are hard on liver has a lot of drug-drug interaction

Keeping Immune system up is main focus. Have to follow strict diet and exercise program.

- Entry inhibitor
  — Enfuvirtide (Fuzeon)
- The client should have regular blood counts to track the CD4+ T-cell levels and the viral load.
- Common side effects of combination therapies include Lipodystrophy, hepatitis, diabetes, pancreatitis, peripheral neuropathy, nephrotoxicity, hepatotoxicity, nausea, vomiting, diarrhea, and GI upset.

Pediatric Nursing Considerations and Diagnostic Evaluation for HIV
Considerations
- Family education focuses on transmission and control of infectious diseases.
- Safety issues include appropriate storage of special medications and equipment.
- Prevention is a key component of HIV education.
- Aggressive pain management is essential.
- Common psychosocial concerns include disclosure of the diagnosis.

Evaluation
- CD4+ cell monitoring tracks progression of the disease.
- For children 18 months of age and older:
  — ELISA for HIV
  — Western blot immunoassay
- For infants younger than 18 months: born to HIV + mothers
  — HIV polymerase chain reaction (PCR)
- Nursing interventions for clients with HIV should focus on preventing infection, promoting proper nutrition, promoting self-care, and supporting counseling efforts.

Cancer

Leukemia
- Acute myelogenous leukemia (AML)
  — Inability of leukocytes to mature; those that do are abnormal
  — Clients usually 60 to 70 years of age
  — Poor prognosis
- Chronic myelogenous leukemia (CML)
  — Abnormal production of granulocytic cells
  — Clients usually 20 to 60 years of age (peak around 45 years)
  — Poor prognosis
- Acute lymphocytic leukemia (ALL)
  — Abnormal leukocytes in blood-forming tissue
  — Usually appears before age 14 years and in older adults
  — Favorable prognosis
- Chronic lymphocytic leukemia (CLL)
  — Increased production of leukocytes and lymphocytes in the bone marrow, spleen, and liver
  — Clients usually 50 to 70 years of age
  — Five-year survival rate is 73% overall

* understand what leukemia means

Nursing Assessment

- General
  — Fever, generalized lymphadenopathy, lethargy
- Integumentary
  — Pallor or jaundice; petechiae, ecchymoses, purpura, reddish brown to purple cutaneous infiltrates, macules, and papules
- Cardiovascular
  — Tachycardia, systolic murmurs
- Gastrointestinal
  — Gingival bleeding and hyperplasia; oral ulcerations, herpes and Candida infections; perirectal irritation and infection; hepatomegaly, splenomegaly
- Neurologic
  — Seizures, disorientation, confusion, decreased coordination, cranial nerve palsies, papilledema
- Musculoskeletal
  — Muscle wasting, bone pain, joint pain

General Nursing Interventions for Clients with Immunodeficiency and/or Bone Marrow Suppression

- Monitor WBC count
- Report fever or S/S of infection to physician as soon as symptoms are recognized
- Teach infection control measures

Hodgkin's Lymphoma
Diagnosis

The primary diagnostic feature of Hodgkin's lymphoma is the presence of Reed-Sternberg cells in biopsy specimens from lymph nodes.

Nursing Assessment

- Weight loss
- Fatigue
- Weakness
- Chills, fever, night sweats
- Tachycardia

Nursing Interventions

- Chemotherapy
- Radiation therapy
- Management of pain caused by tumors
- Pancytopenia
- Fertility
- Secondary malignancies

Non-Hodgkin's Lymphoma
Diagnosis

- MRI, CT scan, and barium enemas

Treatment Modalities

- Chemotherapy (sometimes radiation therapy)
- Monoclonal antibodies
- Symptom management (depending on affected system)

Handwritten margin notes:

A lot of "cancer side effects" are caused by chemo.
But leukemia will usually show signs because of illness first.

WBC is important for anyone who is immunocompromised
Normal count: 5,000 - 10,000
above 10,000 - fighting infection
below 5,000 - immunocompromised "neutropenia"

when all your "labs" are wiped-out.
panculture: culture of everything

23

Nursing Assessment
- Painless lymph node enlargement (lymphadenopathy)
- Depending on where the disease has spread
- Same as Hodgkin's lymphoma

Nursing and Collaborative Management
- Strict aseptic technique
- Protect client from infection
- Monitor for S/S of anemia
- High-nutrient diet
- Emotional support for client and family
- Treatment must be completed to help ensure survival
- Disease is highly curable when diagnosed early and treatment is completed

A client who is receiving chemotherapy has these CBC results: hemoglobin–8.5 g/dL; hematocrit–32%; and WBC count–6,500 cells/mm3. Which meal is the best choice for this client? *Norm*
A. Grilled chicken, rice, fresh fruit salad, milk
B. Broiled steak, whole wheat rolls, spinach salad, coffee
C. Smoked ham, mashed potatoes, applesauce, iced tea
D. Tuna noodle casserole, garden salad, lemonade

HESI Test Question Approach		
Positive?	YES	NO
Key Words		
Rephrase		
Rule Out Choices		
A	B	C	D

Head and Neck Cancer
- Typically squamous cell in origin
- Tumor sites
  — Paranasal sinuses
  — Oral cavity
  — Nasopharynx
  — Oropharynx
  — Larynx
- Disability is great because of the potential loss of voice, disfigurement, and social consequences.
- Head and neck cancer is most common in males older than age 50 and is related to heavy tobacco and alcohol intake.

Lung Cancer
- Number one cancer in the United States!
- Increase in death rates for both men and women is directly related to cigarette smoking.

Nursing Assessment
- Symptoms of lung cancer are not usually apparent until the disease is in the advanced stages.
- Persistent hacking cough may be either dry or productive with blood-tinged sputum.
- Hoarseness
- Dyspnea
- Abnormal chest x-ray
- Positive sputum on cytologic exam

Treatment Modalities

- Chemotherapy
- Radiation therapy
- Surgical intervention
  — Pneumonectomy (removal of entire lung)
  — Lobectomy (segmental resection)

Immediate Postoperative Care

- Promote ventilation and re-expansion of the lung by:
  — Maintaining a clear airway
  — Maintaining the closed drainage system if one is used
- Promote arm exercises to maintain full use on the operative side
- Promote nutrition
- Monitor the incision for bleeding and subcutaneous emphysema

Colorectal Cancer

- The third most common form of cancer and the second leading cause of cancer-related deaths in the United States
  — Adenocarcinoma most common
  — Common metastasis to the liver

Symptoms

- Rectal bleeding
- Change in bowel habits
- Abdominal pain, weight loss, N/V
- Ribbon-like stool
- Sensation of incomplete evacuation

Diagnostic Testing

- Testing of stool for occult blood
- Colonoscopy

Treatment Modalities

- Chemotherapy
- Radiation therapy
- Adjunctive or palliative care

Surgical Intervention

- Bowel resection
- Temporary colostomy
- Permanent colostomy

Postoperative Care Concerns

- Stoma care
  — Loop
  — Double-barrel
  — End stoma
- Incision care
  — Abdominal
  — Perineal
- Packing and drains
  — HemoVac
  — Jackson-Pratt
- Body image
- Patient teaching support

25

Stoma Assessment

- The stoma should be pink.
- Mild to moderate swelling of the stoma is seen for the first 2 to 3 weeks after surgery.
- Be familiar with the pouching system, which includes:
  — Skin barrier
  — Bag or pouch
  — Adhesive
- Help the client cope with the stoma
  — Provide information
  — Teach practical stoma care techniques
- Help the client address concerns regarding social interactions
  — Employment
  — Body image
  — Sexuality

The nurse is caring for a client who is 24 hours postoperative for a hemicolectomy with temporary colostomy placement. On assessment, the nurse finds that the stoma is dry and dark red. Based on this finding, what action should the nurse take?

A. Notify the healthcare provider of the finding.
B. Document the finding in the client's record.
C. Replace the pouch system over the stoma.
D. Put a petrolatum gauze dressing on the stoma.

HESI Test Question Approach			
Positive?		~~YES~~	NO
Key Words On assessment, which action should the nurse take			
Rephrase			
Rule Out Choices			
A	B	C	D

Breast Cancer

- Risks
  — Family history
  — Age
  — Hyperestrogenism
  — Radiation exposure
- Most tumors are discovered through breast self-examination
- Tumors tend to be in the upper outer quadrant
  — Ductal carcinoma
  — Lobar carcinoma
  — Ductal carcinoma in situ
  — Inflammatory breast cancer (most aggressive)
  — Paget's disease (areola and nipple)
- Recommend a mammogram every 1 to 2 years after age 40 and then annually after age 50

Treatment Modalities

- Surgical intervention
  — Mastectomy
  — Modified radical mastectomy
  — Lumpectomy
  — Tissue expansion and breast implants
  — Musculocutaneous flap procedure
- Radiation
- Chemotherapy
- Hormonal therapy
- Biologic targeted therapies
- Monoclonal antibodies

Nursing Assessment

- Hard lump not freely moveable
- Dimpling of the skin
- Change in skin color
- Confirmed by a mammogram and biopsy with frozen sections

Nursing Interventions

- Preoperative
  — Assess expectations
- Postoperative
  — Monitor for bleeding
  — Position arm on operative side on a pillow
  — Do not allow BP cuffs, IVs, or injections on operative side
  — Provide emotional support and recognize the grieving process

Cancer of the Cervix

- Human papillomavirus (HPV) infects the skin and mucous membranes of humans.
- A vaccine for HPV (i.e., Gardasil, Cervarix) has been approved for females ages 9 to 26. Three vaccinations are required over 6 months. Only Gardasil is available for males. In addition to girls and boys aged 11 or 12 years, the CDC recommends HPV vaccination for teenage boys and girls who were not vaccinated when younger; teenage girls and young women through age 26; and teenage boys and young men through age 21.
- HPV infection usually can be detected early with a Pap test.
- Dysplasia is treated with cryosurgery, laser therapy, conization, and possibly hysterectomy.
- Early carcinoma is treated with hysterectomy or intra-cavitary irradiation.
- Late carcinoma is treated with beam irradiation, chemotherapy, and/or pelvic exenteration.

Care of the Client with Radiation Implants

- The client is **not** radioactive.
- Implants do contain radioactive material.
- Place the client in a private room.
- Do not allow pregnant caretakers or pregnant visitors.
- Keep lead-lined container in the room.
- Be aware that the client's secretions may be radioactive.
- Wear a radiation badge when providing care.

A 20-year-old client has been receiving chemotherapy for acute lymphocytic leukemia. Which statement by the client indicates understanding of the nurse's discharge teaching about leukopenia?

A. "I'm relieved that I don't have any activity restrictions."
B. "I'd better wash my hands carefully, because my son can catch leukopenia."
C. "I should avoid close contact with people who might give me an infection."
D. "I need to be careful not to cut myself when shaving, because I may not be able to stop the bleeding."

HESI Test Question Approach		
Positive?	YES	NO
Key Words		
Rephrase		
Rule Out Choices		
A	B	C	D

Ovarian Cancer

- Most important risk factor is a family history of the disease
- Asymptomatic in early stages
- Generalized feeling of abdominal fullness
- Sense of pelvic heaviness
- Loss of appetite
- Change in bowel habits
- Late-stage symptoms
  - Pelvic discomfort
  - Low back pain
  - Abdominal pain
- Leading cause of death from gynecological cancers

Testicular Cancer

Young

- Feeling of heaviness in the lower abdomen
- Painless lump or swelling
- Postoperative orchiectomy
- Observe for bleeding
- Encourage genetic counseling (sperm banking)
- Postoperative management
  - Monitor for urine leaks
  - Avoid rectal manipulation
  - Low-residue diet

Cancer of the Prostate

Old

- Symptoms of urinary obstruction
- Elevated prostate-specific antigen (PSA)
- Surgical removal of the prostate
- Follow-up radiation and chemotherapy
- Assess for headache, vomiting, seizures, aphasia, abnormal CT, MRI, or PET scan

The charge nurse is assigning rooms for four new clients, but only one private room is available on the oncology unit. Which condition indicates that the client should be assigned to the private room?
A. Ovarian cancer (the client is receiving chemotherapy).
B. Breast cancer (the client is receiving external beam irradiation).
C. Prostate cancer (the client just had a transurethral resection).
D. Cervical cancer (the client is receiving intracavitary irradiation).

HESI Test Question Approach		
Positive?	YES	NO
Key Words Which condition indicates – private room		
Rephrase		
Rule Out Choices		
A	B	C	D

Brain Tumor

- Primary malignant tumors can arise in any area of brain tissue.
- Benign tumors can continue to grow and cause problems with ↑ ICP.

Nursing Plans and Interventions
- Similar to those for a client with a head injury
- Major concern is ↑ ICP
- Keep HOB elevated 30 to 40 degrees

Treatment Modalities
- Radiation therapy
- Chemotherapy
- Surgical removal (craniotomy)
- Postoperative care
  — Monitor for ↑ ICP
  — Check for CSF leakage
  — Monitor respiratory status closely
  — Monitor for seizure activity

General Perioperative Care

Preoperative Care
- NPO after midnight before surgery
- Teach coughing and deep breathing, incentive spirometry
- Review methods of pain control

Postoperative Care
A primary goal of postoperative care is to prevent common complications.
- Urinary retention
  — Check for bladder distention
- Pulmonary problems
  — Check breath sounds
  — O_2 saturation
- Decreased peristalsis
  — Paralytic ileus
  — Absent bowel sounds
- Wound dehiscence
  — Wound evisceration

A client who is postoperative for a colectomy complains, "I just felt a popping right after I coughed." The PN notes a large amount of serosanguineous drainage and the intestines protruding slightly from the incision. The PN should immediately implement which priority intervention(s)? (Select all that apply.)
A. Encourage the client to turn and deep breathe while splinting the opening.
B. Cover the wound with a moist, sterile normal saline dressing.
C. Document the appearance of loops of bowel through the wound.
D. Reinsert the organs and apply a firm pressure dressing.
E. Place the client in a low Fowler's position with the knees bent.
F. Contact the charge nurse and call the healthcare provider.

HESI Test Question Approach			
Positive?		YES	NO
Key Words	Priority		
Rephrase			
Rule Out Choices			
A	B	C	D

Chapter **3** **Clinical Concepts and Mechanisms of Disease for the Practical Nurse**

A client expresses anxiety to the PN about upcoming surgery. Which response by the PN is likely to be most supportive of the client?

A. "Tell me what has been shared with you about the surgery."
B. "Let me review the postoperative care you'll receive after surgery."
C. "Don't worry, your surgeon has the best record of success."
D. "I had surgery just like that, and I'm fine."

HESI Test Question Approach

Positive?		YES	NO
Key Words	Anxiety about upcoming surgery		
Rephrase			
Rule Out Choices			
A	B	C	D

The LPN checks a client's abdominal surgical incision for signs of infection. Which sign or symptom would indicate an infection? (Select all that apply.)

A. The client refuses to cough and deep breathe as directed.
B. The client complains of a pain level of 7 on a scale of 1 to 10.
C. A moderate amount of serosanguineous drainage is present on the gauze dressing.
D. The client complains of chills and tremors.
E. The client's vital signs are: temperature–100.4° F (38.° C); pulse–106 beats/min; respirations–20 breaths/min.

HESI Test Question Approach

Positive?		YES	NO
Key Words			
Rephrase			
Rule Out Choices			
A	B	C	D

4 Advanced Clinical Concepts and Disaster Management

Acute Conditions

Shock
Stages
- Stage 1: Initial
  — Agitation (among early signs)
  — Restlessness
  — ↑ Heart rate
  — Cool, pale skin
- Stage 2: Compensatory
  — Cardiac output < 4-6 L/min
  — BP systolic < 100 mm Hg
  — ↓ Urinary output
  — Confusion
  — Cerebral perfusion < 70 mm Hg
- Stage 3: Progressive
  — Edema
  — Excessively low BP
  — Dysrhythmia
  — Weak, thready pulses
- Stage 4: Irreversible
  — Profound hypotension
  — No response to vasopressors
  — Slowing heart rate
  — Multiple organ failure
  — Severe hypoxemia

Types of Shock
- Hypovolemic
  — Most common
  — Related to internal or external blood/fluid loss
- Cardiogenic
  — Pump failure
  — Results in ↓ cardiac output
- Vasogenic (anaphylactic, neurogenic, septic shock)
  — Excessive vasodilation and impaired distribution of blood flow
  — Failure of arteriolar resistance
  — *sepsis*

Treatment for Shock
- Cause of shock dictates type of treatment
  — Correct decreased tissue perfusion and restore cardiac output
    - Optimize oxygenation and ventilation
    - Establish fluid resuscitation
      □ Volume expanders for hypovolemia
        ◆ In cardiogenic shock, volume expanders may precipitate pulmonary edema

— Drug therapy
  - Restore cardiac function based on effect of shock on preload, afterload, and contractility
    - Replace blood volume or fluid loss
    - Administer medications
      - Vasodilators
      - Vasoconstrictors

Collaborative and Nursing Management

- Monitor
  - Vital signs
  - Mental status
  - Fluid status
  - Urine output

An elderly client with a percutaneous gastrostomy feeding tube is admitted from a nursing home to the hospital. The client has altered mental status, dehydration, and fever. In caring for this client, the nurse should be alert to which priority condition?

A. Cardiogenic shock
B. Acute renal failure
C. Glomerulonephritis
D. Urinary tract infection

HESI Test Question Approach		
Positive?	YES	NO
Key Words mental status —elderly, dehydration, + fever		
Rephrase		
Rule Out Choices		
A	B	C	D

Cascade of Sepsis

Septic shock is one component of the systemic inflammatory response syndrome (SIRS). The syndrome starts with an infection that progresses to *bacteremia,* then *sepsis,* then *severe sepsis,* then *septic shock,* and finally multiple organ dysfunction syndrome (MODS).

SIRS is a systemic inflammatory response to an assortment of insults, including sepsis, ischemia, infarction, and injury. Generalized inflammation occurs in organs remote from the initial insult.

MODS is the failure of two or more organ systems in an acutely ill client such that homeostasis cannot be maintained without intervention. MODS results from SIRS.

Nursing and Collaborative Management

- The prognosis for the client with MODS is poor.
- The most important goal is to prevent the progression of SIRS to MODS.
- The nursing role is attentive assessment and ongoing monitoring to detect early signs of organ dysfunction.

Collaborative care focuses on:
- Prevention strategies
- Early screening for subtle changes in HR, systolic BP, respiratory rate, oxygen saturation, and urinary output, as well as central nervous system changes
- Serum lactate level

- Prevention and treatment of infection
  — Blood culture before starting antibiotics
  — Broad-spectrum antibiotics within 1 to 3 hours of admission
- Maintenance of tissue oxygenation
- Nutritional and metabolic support
- Support of individual failing organs

Disseminated Intravascular Coagulation (DIC)

- DIC is a serious coagulopathy resulting from over-stimulation of clotting and anticlotting processes in response to disease or injury, including septicemia, obstetric complication, malignancies, tissue trauma, transfusion reaction, burns, shock, and snakebite.
- Hypercoagulability is followed by a deficiency in clotting factors, with subsequent hypocoagulability and hemorrhaging.
  — DIC may lead to uncontrollable hemorrhage.
- The D-dimer assay measures the degree of fibrinolysis.
- DIC requires astute, ongoing assessment.
  — Early detection of bleeding, both occult and overt, must be a primary goal.
  — Assess the client for signs of external and internal bleeding.
  — Active attention to manifestations of the syndrome is crucial.
- Appropriate treatment measures, which can be challenging and sometimes paradoxical, may include:
  — Heparin infusion
  — Blood and FFP transfusions and cryoprecipitate

Body cannot determine if it should be clotting or bleeding. Most common in ICU and maternity patients.

Heparin because clotting is biggest concern.

Acute Respiratory Distress Syndrome (ARDS)

- ARDS is considered to be present if the client has:
  — Refractory hypoxemia
  — New bilateral interstitial or alveolar infiltrates on a chest x-ray film (often called "whiteout" or "white lung")
  — Pulmonary artery wedge pressure of 18 mm Hg or lower with no evidence of heart failure
  — A predisposing condition for ARDS within 48 hours of clinical manifestations
- ARDS is marked by alveolar capillary membrane damage with subsequent leakage of fluids into the interstitial spaces and alveoli.
- As ARDS progresses, profound respiratory distress develops, requiring endotracheal intubation and PPV.

Nursing Assessment

- Dyspnea
- Scattered crackles
- Intercostal retractions
- Pink frothy sputum
- Cyanosis
- Hypoxemia
- Hypercapnia
- Respiratory acidosis
- Impaired gas exchange
- Increased secretions
- Decreased cardiac output

Nursing and Collaborative Management

- The overall goals for a client with ARDS are:
  — Pao_2 of at least 60 mm Hg
  — Adequate lung ventilation to maintain normal pH
- The goals for a client recovering from ARDS are:
  — Pao_2 within normal limits for age or baseline values on room air
  — $Sao_2 > 90\%$
  — Patent airway
  — Clear lungs on auscultation
- Positive end-expiratory pressure (PEEP) creates positive pressure at end exhalation and restores functional residual capacity (FRC)

Delirium

- Delirium is an acute state of confusion, commonly occurring in the elderly, that may indicate an impending change in condition (e.g., sepsis).
- Risk factors
  — Use of opioids and/or corticosteroids
  — Drug or alcohol abuse
  — UTI, fluid and electrolyte imbalance
  — Postoperative, ICU, or emergent delirium
  — Sleep deprivation, advanced age, or vision and hearing impairment

Nursing and Collaborative Management

- Monitor neurological status on an ongoing basis
- Provide a low-stimulation environment
- Approach the client slowly and from the front
- Provide the appropriate level of supervision/surveillance
- Reorient the client and communicate with simple statements
- Consider management with neuroleptic drugs (e.g., haloperidol [Haldol]) when indicated
- Encourage family visibility and support

Life Support

CPR and Choking Basics (Adults)

- Cardiac arrest is the most common event requiring CPR
- C-A-B: Chest compressions—Airway—Breathing
- High-quality chest compressions are vital
- Push hard and push fast
- Adults: 100 compressions/min

In-Hospital Cardiac Arrest

Initiate CPR according to BCLS guidelines.

- Determine unresponsiveness
- Activate emergency response or cardiac arrest team
- Call for AED and/or emergency crash cart (do not leave client)
  — If a pulse is not identified within 10 seconds, then:
    - Maintain 30 compressions:2 breaths ratio
    - Establish an airway
    - Ventilate with 2 breaths via manual resuscitation (breathing) bag (Ambu)
    - Apply quick-look paddles or AED to determine whether defibrillation is necessary; defibrillate as indicated according to hospital policies and procedures

CPR and Choking Basics (Neonates and Children Age 1 to 8 Years)

- Most common indications for CPR in children are not the same as for adults.
- Neonates and infants: hypoxia, hypoglycemia, hypothermia, acidosis, hypercoagulability
- Children: respiratory arrest, prolonged hypoxemia secondary to respiratory insult or shock, including septic shock
- Guidelines vary based on age of child.
- If no response occurs, call a "code" or cardiac arrest in order to initiate response of cardiac arrest team. Obtain AED or Emergency Crash Cart with defibrillator.
- Check for pulse
  — Infant <1 year old brachial pulse
  — Children 1 year to puberty carotid or femoral

Compressions

- Compressions in infants cover at least one third of the anterior/posterior diameter of the chest; depth is 1½ inches in most infants.
- Compressions in children cover at least one third of the anterior/posterior diameter of the chest; depth is 2 inches in most children.
  — 30 compressions to 2 breaths with one rescuer
  — 15 compressions to 1 breath with 2 rescuers
  — Deliver each breath over 1 second (avoid excess ventilation (gastric inflation)

For up-to-date information on FBOA and CPR, see the American Heart Association website for CPR guidelines: *www.heart.org/HEARTORG/*.

The practical nurse is caring for a client who suddenly loses consciousness. The nurse performs which intervention first?

A. Quickly go to the nurses' station and ask the charge nurse to call a code.
B. Obtain a defibrillator from an adjacent nursing unit.
C. Call for help and initiate cardiopulmonary resuscitation (CPR).
D. Start oxygen by cannula at 10 L/min and raise the head of the bed.

HESI Test Question Approach		
Positive?	~~YES~~	NO
Key Words		
Rephrase		
Rule Out Choices		
~~A~~	~~B~~	C ~~D~~

Disaster Management

- Nurses are active members of teams in the event of a biological, chemical, radioactive, mass trauma, or natural disaster.
- Nurses play a role at all three levels of disaster management (primary, secondary, tertiary).

Preparedness ... Response ... Recovery

- Levels of prevention in disaster management
  — *Primary:* Planning, training, educating personnel and the public
  — *Secondary:* Triage, treatment, shelter supervision
  — *Tertiary:* Follow-up, recovery assistance, prevention of future disasters

Bioterrorism

- Review exposure information, assessment findings, and treatment for various agents.
- Questions may deal with disasters and bioterrorism as they affect the individual victim, families, and the community.

The PN receives change of shift report about a client who is 6 hours postoperative. The vital signs are: BP, 106/74; temp, 98.6° F; pulse -78- respiration 14. Urine output is 300 mL/6 hr. Three hours later, the PN suspects that the client is developing shock. What signs indicate the development of early hypovolemic shock? (Select all that apply.)

(A) Apical pulse rate, 92/min
B. Temp—99.0° F
(C) Urine output—100 mL/3-hr
(D) Respiratory rate—25/min
(E) Anxiousness
F. Lethargy

HESI Test Question Approach		
Positive?	YES	NO
Key Words		
Rephrase		
Rule Out Choices		

A	B	C	D

5 Oxygenation, Ventilation, Transportation, and Perfusion

A male client who is 1 day postoperative after a left pneumonectomy is lying on his right side with the head of bed (HOB) elevated 10 degrees. The PN assesses his respiratory rate at 32 breaths/min. What action should the nurse take first?

A. Elevate the head of the bed.
B. Assist the client into the supine position.
C. Measure the O_2 saturation.
D. Administer PRN morphine IV.

HESI Test Question Approach			
Positive?		YES	NO
Key Words			
Rephrase			
Rule Out Choices			
A	B	C	D

Principles of Chest Tube: Water or Dry Seal Management

- Chest tubes are inserted into the pleural space to remove air and fluid and to allow the lung to re-expand.
- There are three compartments or chambers to a chest collection drainage system.
  — Collection chamber
    • Collects air and fluid from the pleural or mediastinal space.
    • Fluid remains; air is vented to the second compartment, or water seal chamber.
  — Water seal chamber
    • Contains 2 cm of water, which prevents backflow and acts as a one-way valve.
    • Shows *tidaling,* or water level fluctuations; fluid should move upward with each inspiration and downward with each expiration.
  — Suction control chamber
    • Water suction uses 20 cm of water to aid in draining air or fluid from the chest.
    • Dry suction provides a safe and effective level of vacuum by continuously balancing the forces of suction and atmosphere.

Nursing and Collaborative Management

- Keep all tubing coiled loosely below chest level, with connections tight and taped.
- Monitor the fluid drainage; mark the time of measurement and the fluid level.
- Observe for air bubbling in the water seal chamber and tidaling.
- Replace the unit when full.
- Chest tubes are not clamped routinely.
- If the chest tube becomes dislodged, cover the area with a dry, sterile dressing. If an air leak is noted, tape the dressing on three sides only; this allows air to escape and prevents the formation of a tension pneumothorax. Notify the healthcare provider.

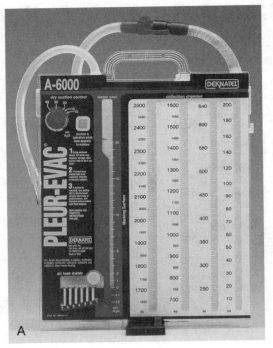

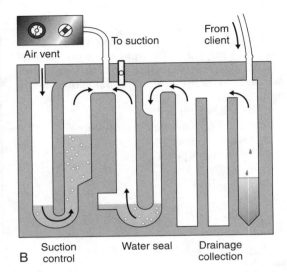

Figure 5-1 Chest tubes are used to remove or drain blood or air from the intrapleural space, to expand the lung after surgery, or to restore subatmospheric pressure to the thoracic cavity. Many brands of commercial chest drainage systems are available; all are based on the traditional three-bottle water seal system. **A,** Commonly used disposable chest drainage system. **B,** Diagram of the chambers of a water seal chest drainage system. (From Linton A: *Introduction to medical-surgical nursing,* ed 5, St Louis, 2010, Saunders.)

The husband of a 94-year-old woman tells the clinic PN that his wife has become increasingly confused over the past few days and has developed a cough. Which assessment should the nurse perform first?

A. Jugular vein distention
B. Skin turgor
C. Oxygen saturation
D. Pupillary response to light

HESI Test Question Approach		
Positive?	**YES**	**NO**
Key Words		
Rephrase		
Rule Out Choices		
A	B	C	D

Pneumonia

Pathophysiology

- Results in inflammation of lung tissue, causing consolidation of exudate
- Pathogens: bacterial (gram negative most severe), viral (rare), fungal
- Host's physical status
- Aspiration
- Inhalation
- Hypostatic

Nursing Assessment

- Tachypnea
- Fever of abrupt onset
- Dyspnea
- Cyanosis
- Mental status changes
- Crackles, decreased breath sounds
- Dullness with percussion

Nursing and Collaborative Management

- Hand washing to reduce cross-contamination
- Antibiotics
- Isolation if prescribed
- Administer fluids
- Manage pain
- Monitor oxygenation (humidified to loosen secretions)

Antiinfective Medications

- Penicillins
  - Semisynthetic penicillins
    - Oxacillin
  - Antipseudomonal penicillins
    - Piperacillin (Pipracil)
- Tetracyclines
  - Doxycycline hyclate (Vibramycin)
- Aminoglycosides
  - Gentamicin sulfate (Garamycin)
- Cephalosporins
  - Ceftriaxone (Rocephin)
- Macrolides
  - Clarithromycin (Biaxin)
- Fluoroquinolones
  - Ciprofloxacin (Cipro)

Chronic Airflow Limitation (CAL)

- Asthma—a reversible disease
- Chronic obstructive pulmonary disease (COPD)—a chronic, progressive disease
  - Emphysema
  - Chronic bronchitis

COPD Etiology/Precipitating Factors

- Cigarette smoking
- Environmental/occupational exposure
- Genetic predisposition

Chronic Bronchitis

- Pathophysiology
  - Chronic sputum with cough production on a daily basis for a minimum of 3 months/year
  - Chronic hypoxemia/cor pulmonale
  - Increase in mucus, cilia production
  - Increase in bronchial wall thickness (obstructs air flow)
  - Exacerbations usually due to infection
  - ↑ V/Q abnormalities
  - ↑ CO_2 retention/acidemia
  - ↑ Pulmonary artery pressure (PAP) = cor pulmonale
  - Reduced responsiveness of respiratory center to hypoxemic stimuli

Emphysema

- Abnormal enlargement of the air spaces distal to the terminal alveolar walls
- Increased dyspnea/work of breathing
- Reduced gas exchange surface area
- Increased air trapping (increased anterior-posterior diameter)
- Decreased capillary network
- Increased work/increased O_2 consumption

COPD Assessment Data

- Inspection
  - Bronchitis
    - Right-sided heart failure
    - Cyanosis
    - Distended neck veins
  - Emphysema
    - Noncyanotic
    - Thin appearance
    - Pursed-lip breathing
- Auscultation
  - Bronchitis
    - Crackles
    - Rhonchi
    - Expiratory wheezes
  - Emphysema
    - Distant breath sounds
    - Quiet breath sounds
    - Wheezes

COPD Nursing and Collaborative Management

- Lowest O_2 to prevent CO_2 retention
  - Respiratory drive based on O_2 levels
- Monitor for signs and symptoms (S/S) of fluid overload
- Baseline ABGs for CO_2 retainers
- Teach client pursed-lip breathing
- Orthopneic position

Reactive Airway Disease
Asthma

- Inflammatory disorder of the airways characterized by an exaggerated bronchoconstrictor response to a wide variety of stimuli:
  - Allergens
  - Environmental irritants
  - Cold air
  - Exercise
  - β-blockers
  - Respiratory infection
  - Emotional stress
  - Reflux esophagitis

Drug Therapy for COPD and Asthma:
Bronchodilators
β₂-Adrenergic Agonists

- Inhaled: short acting
  - Metaproterenol (Alupent, Metaprel)—nebulizer, oral tablets, elixir, metered-dose inhaler (MDI)

- Albuterol (Proventil, Proventil, Ventolin, HFA, Salbutamol, Volmax)—nebulizer, MDI, oral tablets, Rotahaler
- Pirbuterol (Maxair)—MDI
- Terbutaline (Bricanyl, Brethine)—oral tablets, nebulizer, subcutaneous, MDI
- Bitolterol (Tornalate)—MDI, nebulizer
■ Inhaled: long acting
- Salmeterol (Serevent)—dry powder inhaler (DPI)
- Formoterol (Foradil)—DPI
■ Immediate acting
- Epinephrine (Adrenalin)—subcutaneous
■ Corticosteroids
- Hydrocortisone (Solu-Cortef)—IV
- Methylprednisolone (Medrol, Solu-Medrol)—oral
- Prednisone IV
- Beclomethasone (Vanceril, Beclovent, Vanceril DS, Qvar, Qvar HFA)—oral
- Flunisolide (AeroBid, AeroBid-M)
- Fluticasone (Flovent HFA, Flovent Diskus)
- Budesonide (Pulmicort Turbuhaler, Pulmicort Respules)
- Mometasone (Asmanex Twisthaler)
■ Anticholinergics
- Short-acting ipratropium (Atrovent)—nebulizer, MDI
- Long-acting tiotropium (Spiriva)—DPI
■ Mast cell stabilizers
- Cromolyn (Intal)—nebulizer, MDI
- Nedocromil (Tilade)—MDI
■ IgE Antagonist omalizumab (Xolair)—subcutaneous injection
■ Leukotriene modifiers
- Leukotriene receptor blockers
  • Zafirlukast (Accolate)—oral tablets
  • Montelukast (Singulair)—oral tablets, chewable tablets, oral granules
- Leukotriene inhibitor
  • Zileuton (Zyflo)—oral tablets
■ Methylxanthines
- IV, Oral: Aminophylline (rarely used)—IV infusion, oral tablets, elixir, sustained-release tablets
- Oral: Theophylline (Elixophyllin, Quibron, Slo-bid, Theochron, Theolair, Theo-24, Uniphyl)—liquid, oral tablets and capsules
■ Combination agents
- Ipratropium/albuterol (Combivent, DuoNeb)—MDI, nebulizer
- Fluticasone/salmeterol (Advair)—DPI
- Budesonide/formoterol (Symbicort)—MDI

Nursing Assessment
■ Dyspnea, wheezing, chest tightness
■ Assess precipitating factors
■ Medication history

Nursing Interventions
■ Monitor respirations and assess breath sounds
■ Monitor oxygen saturation
■ Monitor mental status
■ Perform chest physiotherapy
■ Assess peripheral pulses and warmth and color of extremities

- Position for maximum ventilation
- Encourage slow, pursed-lip breathing
- Encourage abdominal breathing
- Administer humidified oxygen therapy

The PN palpates a crackling sensation of the skin around the insertion site of a chest tube in a client who has had thoracic surgery. What action should the nurse take?
A. Make sure the client returns to surgery
B. Prepare for insertion of a larger chest tube
C. Increase the water seal suction pressure
D. Continue to monitor the condition

HESI Test Question Approach		
Positive?	**YES**	**NO**
Key Words		
Rephrase		
Rule Out Choices		
A	**B**	**C**	**D**

Tuberculosis (TB)

TB is an infectious disease caused by the bacillus *Mycobacterium tuberculosis* or the tubercle bacillus, an acid-fast organism.

Resurgence of TB in the United States
- Related to HIV infection
- Multidrug-resistant TB (MDR-TB)
- Seen disproportionately in the poor, underserved, and minorities

Nursing Assessment
- Low-grade fever
- Pallor
- Chills
- Night sweats
- Easy fatigability
- Anorexia
- Weight loss

Nursing Interventions
- Airborne precautions isolation
- Medication regimen
  — Isoniazid (INH therapy)
  — Pyridoxine (vitamin B_6)
  — Rifampin (Rifadin)
  — Pyrazinamide
  — Taken as prescribed 9 to 12 months
  — Teach side effects

TB Drugs
First-Line Drugs
- Bacteriocidal against rapidly dividing cells and/or against semidormant bacteria
- Isoniazid (INH): Clinical hepatitis, fulminant hepatitis, peripheral neurotoxicity
- Rifampin (Rifadin): Cutaneous reactions, GI disturbance (nausea, anorexia, abdominal pain), flulike syndrome, hepatotoxicity, immunological reactions, orange discoloration of bodily fluids (sputum, urine, sweat, tears)

- Ethambutol (Myambutol): Retrobulbar neuritis (decreased red-green color discrimination), skin rash
- Rifabutin (Mycobutin): Hematological toxicity, GI symptoms, polyarthralgias, pseudojaundice, orange discoloration of bodily fluids
- Pyrazinamide (PZA): Hepatotoxicity, GI symptoms (nausea, vomiting), polyarthralgias, skin rash, hyperuricemia, dermatitis
- Rifapentine (Priftin)

Pulmonary Embolus

Typically a blood clot enters the venous circulation and lodges in the pulmonary vasculature.

Risk Factors for VTE Leading to PE
- Prolonged immobility
- Central venous catheters
- Surgery
- Obesity
- Advancing age
- Conditions that increase blood clotting
- History of thromboembolism
- Smoking, BCP, pregnancy

Signs and Symptoms
- Dyspnea, tachypnea, tachycardia, chest pain
- Apprehension, restlessness, feeling of impending doom
- Cough, hemoptysis, diaphoresis
- Crackles, pleural friction rub
- Decreased arterial oxygen saturation (Sao_2), respiratory alkalosis, then respiratory acidosis
- Diagnosed by physical findings and computed tomography (CT) and transesophageal echocardiography (TEE) results

Nursing and Collaborative Management
Prevention
- Range-of-motion exercises
- Ambulate and turn
- Use antiembolism and pneumatic compression stockings
- Assess peripheral circulation
- Administer prescribed prophylactic low-dose anticoagulant and antiplatelet drugs
- Teach the client and family about precautions
- Encourage smoking cessation

Acute Management
- Oxygen therapy
- Monitor ABGs and pulse oximetry
- Check vital signs, lung sounds, and cardiac and respiratory status
- Anticoagulants prevent embolus enlargement and prevent new clots from forming; used with caution in a client with active bleeding, stroke, and recent trauma
- Heparin is usually used unless the PE is massive or occurs with hemodynamic instability
- Alteplase (Activase, tPA), fibrinolytic drug
- Therapeutic PTT values usually range from 1.5 to 2.5 times

- Both heparin and fibrinolytic drugs are high-alert drugs
- Embolectomy
- Inferior vena cava filtration with placement of a vena cava filter

Hematological Problems
Anemia
- Decreased erythrocyte production
- Decreased hemoglobin synthesis
  — Iron deficiency anemia
  — Thalassemias (decreased globin synthesis)
  — Sideroblastic anemia (decreased porphyrin)
- Defective DNA synthesis
  — Cobalamin (vitamin B_{12}) deficiency
  — Folic acid deficiency
- Decreased number of erythrocyte precursors
  — Aplastic anemia
- Anemia of myeloproliferative diseases (e.g., leukemia) and myelodysplasia
- Chronic diseases or disorders
- Chemotherapy
- Blood loss
  — Acute
  — Trauma
- Blood vessel rupture
- Chronic gastritis
- Menstrual flow
- Hemorrhoids
- Increased erythrocyte destruction

Nursing Assessment
- Pallor
- Fatigue
- Exercise intolerance
- Tachycardia
- Dyspnea
- Risk factors
  — Diet low in iron
  — Vitamin B_{12} deficiency
  — History of bleeding
  — Certain medications
  — Hgb < 10, Hct < 36, RBCs < 4

Hypertension (HTN)
- Persistent BP elevation > 140/90 mm Hg
- Risk factors
  — Nonmodifiable: Family history, gender, age, ethnicity
  — Modifiable: Use of alcohol, tobacco, caffeine; sedentary lifestyle; obesity

Medications
- Diuretics
  — Thiazides, metolazone (Zaroxolyn)
- Antihypertensive
  — Minipress, Corgard, Tenormin, Catapres
- ACE inhibitors
  — Zestril
- Calcium channel blockers
  — Cardizem

44

HTN Education

- Number one cause of stroke (cerebrovascular accident [CVA]) is noncompliance with HTN medications.

Coronary Artery Disease (CAD)

- Prevalent etiologies of CAD
  — Atherosclerosis—partially or completely blocked coronary arteries
  — Coronary vasospasm
  — Microvascular angina
- CAD results in ischemia and infarction of myocardial tissue.
- Left anterior descending artery (LAD) is most commonly affected.
- CAD remains the number one health problem in the United States.

Client Education

- Risk factor reduction
  — Smoking cessation
  — Weight reduction
  — Physical activity

Heart Failure
Etiology

- CAD, prior MI
- Chronic HTN
- Cardiomyopathy—dilated
- Idiopathic
- Thyroid
- Diabetes
  — Restrictive
  — Ischemic
- Valvular and congenital heart disease
- Pulmonary diseases

Left-Sided Heart Failure (LHF)

- Causes: LV infarct, cardiomyopathy
- Symptoms: Dyspnea, cough, fluid accumulation in the lungs
- Signs: Tachycardia, inspiratory rales beginning at lung bases, expiratory wheezes due to bronchospasms (misdiagnosed with asthma)
- Laboratory findings: ABGs reveal hypoxemia; chest x-ray study shows pulmonary edema or pleural effusions

Right-Sided Heart Failure (RHF) Systemic Congestion

- Causes: LHF, RV infarct, pulmonary or tricuspid valve disease, pulmonary HTN, COPD, PE
- Symptoms: Dyspnea on exertion, fatigue, weight gain, fluid retention
- Signs: Increased central venous pressure (CVP), jugular venous distention (JVD), hepatomegaly, ascites, peripheral or sacral edema; pleural and pericardial effusions also common

Sodium and Volume Homeostasis
- As CO decreases, renal perfusion decreases.
- This activates the renin-angiotensin system and causes fluid retention.

Pharmacological Management
- Angiotensin-converting enzyme (ACE) inhibitors
  — Captopril
  — Enalapril
  — Fosinopril
  — Lisinopril
  — Quinapril
  — Ramipril
  — Perindopril
  — Benazepril
- Diuretics
  — Loop diuretics
    - Furosemide
    - Bumetanide
    - Torsemide
  — Thiazides
    - Thiazide-related drug: metolazone
- Aldosterone antagonists
  — Spironolactone
  — Eplerenone
- Inotropes
  — Digoxin
  — Dobutamine
- β-blockers
  — Metoprolol
  — Carvedilol
  — Bisoprolol
- Angiotensin II receptor blockers
  — Losartan
  — Candesartan
  — Valsartan
- Vasodilators
  — Nitrates: isosorbide dinitrate
  — Hydralazine
  — Nitroprusside
  — Prazosin
- Dopamine agonist
  — Dopamine
- Analgesics
  — Morphine sulfate
- Anticoagulants
  — Warfarin
  — Aspirin

Nursing Management
- Activity
  — Strongly encourage regular exercise, which improves the function of skeletal muscle more than changes in myocardial function
- Diet
  — Limit sodium intake
  — Restrict fluids only if $Na^+ < 132$ mg/dL
  — Avoid excessive fluids
  — Avoid alcohol, which depresses myocardial contractility
  — With CAD: low cholesterol, low fat, low Na^+

The PN is administering 0900 medications to three clients on a telemetry unit when the unlicensed assistive personnel (UAP) reports that another client is complaining of a sudden onset of substernal discomfort. What action should the PN take?

A. Ask the UAP to obtain the client's vital signs.
B. Assess the client's discomfort.
C. Advise the client to rest in bed.
D. Observe the client's ECG pattern.

HESI Test Question Approach			
Positive?		YES	NO
Key Words			
Rephrase			
Rule Out Choices			
A	B	C	D

Angina

- Varies from mild to severe, transient to prolonged; gradual or sudden in onset
- May radiate to either arm, shoulder, jaw, neck, or epigastric area
- Other S/S: Dyspnea, tachycardia, palpitations, nausea and vomiting, fatigue, diaphoresis, pallor, syncope
- Usually subsides with rest or nitroglycerin
- Often precipitated by exercise, exposure to cold, heavy meal, stress, intercourse

Diet Therapy

- Modify diet to reduce serum cholesterol and serum triglycerides
- Maintain ideal body weight
- Restrict daily cholesterol intake to < 200 mg/day

Cholesterol-Lowering Drugs

- May be initiated if modifying diet is unsuccessful
  — Atorvastatin (Lipitor)
  — Lovastatin (Mevacor)
  — Pravastatin (Pravachol)
  — Rosuvastatin (Crestor)
  — Simvastatin (Zocor)
  — Ezetiemibe (Zetia)
  — Gemfibrozil (Lopid)
  — Niacin (nicotinic acid)

Oxygen

- Administer at 4 to 6 L/min to assist in oxygenating myocardial tissue

Nitroglycerin

- Dilates the coronary arteries
- Increases blood flow to the damaged area of the myocardium
- Dosage:
  — 0.4 mg/tablet
  — 1 tab sublingual every 5 min × 3 doses

Morphine Sulfate

- Analgesic
- ↓ Anxiety
- ↓ Tachypnea
- Relaxes bronchial smooth muscle
- Improves gas exchange

Thrombolytic Therapy

- Useful when infarction is diagnosed early
- Streptokinase and tPA
  — Administer IV
  — Most effective if given within 6 hours of onset of chest pain
- Heparin therapy usually follows thrombolytic therapy

β-Blockers

- Decrease heart rate
- Reduce workload of the heart
- Decrease oxygen demand of the myocardium

Calcium Channel Blockers

- Decrease conduction through the AV node
- Slow the heart rate
- Decrease oxygen demand of the myocardium

Medical Interventions

- Percutaneous transluminal coronary angioplasty (PTCA)
  — Balloon angioplasty
- Intracoronary stents
- Coronary artery bypass graft (CABG)

Acute Myocardial Infarction

- Destruction of myocardial tissue as a result of lack of blood and oxygen supply
- Begins with occlusion of the coronary artery
- Ischemia, injury, infarction

Ischemia

- Caused by reduction in blood flow and oxygen supply to the coronary arteries
- Results in injury if not reversed
- Duration of 20 minutes or longer is sufficient to produce irreversible tissue damage

Injury

- Prolonged interruption of oxygen supply and nutrients
- Cells are still salvageable

Infarction

- Tissue necrosis and death
- Irreversible damage
- Scar tissue (no electrical stimulation or contractility)
- Healing process begins within 24 hours

Complications

- Up to 90% of clients suffer complications from MI, including:
  — Dysrhythmias
  — Cardiac failure
  — Cardiogenic shock
  — Thromboembolism
  — Ventricular rupture

Signs and Symptoms

- Pain
  - Sudden-onset severity increases
  - May persist for hours or days; may not be relieved by rest or nitroglycerin
  - Heavy/constrictive
  - Located behind the sternum
  - May radiate to the arms, back, neck, or jaw
- Skin—cool, clammy
- Pulse—rapid, irregular, feeble

A client complains of a severe headache after receiving nitroglycerin 0.4 mg SL for angina. What prescription should the PN administer?
A. A second dose of nitroglycerin
B. A scheduled dose of low-dose aspirin
C. A PRN dose of acetaminophen PO
D. A PRN dose of morphine sulfate IM

Atypical Symptoms

- Women
  - Discomfort rather than pain
  - Shortness of breath
  - Extreme fatigue
- Clients with diabetes
  - Asymptomatic
  - Neuropathy
  - Dyspnea
- Elderly clients
  - Confusion/delirium
  - Change in mental status
  - Dizziness
  - Shortness of breath

Nursing and Collaborative Management

- Overall goal is to preserve myocardial tissue
- Drug therapy
  - Oxygen
  - Nitroglycerin
  - Morphine
  - Thrombolytic therapy
  - Other medications
- Angioplasty and stents
  - Used if drug therapy is unsuccessful
- Coronary artery bypass graft
  - Used for severe coronary artery disease
  - May be emergent or elective procedure

HESI Test Question Approach			
Positive?		YES	NO
Key Words			
Rephrase			
Rule Out Choices			
A	B	C	D

Dysrhythmias: Interpretation and Management

- Standard ECG using 12 leads
  — Provides best overall evaluation
- Telemetry
  — Usually uses three leads that show one view of the heart
- Holter monitor
  — Usually worn for 24 hours to provide a continuous reading

Electrocardiogram (ECG)

- P wave
  — Atrial depolarization
- QRS complex
  — Ventricular depolarization
  — Normal: <0.11 second
- ST segment
  — Early ventricular repolarization
- PR interval
  — Time for impulse to travel through SA node
  — Normal: 0.12 to 0.20 second
- R-R interval
  — Measures regularity of the heartbeat

Dysrhythmias

- Client may be asymptomatic until cardiac output is altered.
- Client may complain of palpitations, syncope, pain, dyspnea, diaphoresis.
- Changes occur in pulse rate/rhythm and ECG.
- Always treat the client—NOT the monitor!

Atrial Dysrhythmias

- A-fib (atrial fibrillation)
  — Chaotic activity in the AV node
  — No true P waves visible
  — Irregular ventricular rhythm
  — Risk for CVA
  — Anticoagulant therapy necessary
- Atrial flutter
  — Sawtoothed waveform
  — Fluttering in chest
  — Ventricular rhythm regular
- Cardioversion may be used to treat either atrial dysrhythmia.

Ventricular Dysrhythmias

- V-tach (ventricular tachycardia)
  — Wide, bizarre QRS complex
  — Assess whether client has a pulse
  — Is cardiac output impaired?
  — Prepare for synchronized cardioversion
  — Administer antiarrhythmic drugs
- V-fib (ventricular fibrillation)
  — Cardiac emergency
  — No cardiac output
  — Start cardiopulmonary resuscitation (CPR)
  — Defibrillate as quickly as possible
  — Administer antiarrhythmic drugs

Common Medications used in Treatment of CAD

- Antiplatelet
  — Acetylsalicylic acid (ASA)
  — Clopidogrel (Plavix)
- β-blockers
  — Atenolol (Tenormin)
  — Metoprolol (Lopressor, Toprol)
- Nitrates
  — Nitroglycerin
  — Nitroprusside
- Calcium channel blockers
  — Diltiazem (Cardizem)
  — Verapamil (Calan, Isoptin)
- Thrombolytics
  — Alteplase (recombinant tPA) (Activase)
  — Reteplase (rPA) (Retavase)
  — Tenecteplase (TNK-tPA)
  — Streptokinase (Streptase)
- Anticoagulants
  — Unfractionated heparin
  — Low-molecular-weight heparin (LMWH) (enoxaparin [Lovenox])
- ACE inhibitors
  — Captopril (Capoten)
  — Enalapril (Vasotec)
  — Benazepril (Lotensin)
- Analgesics
  — Morphine sulfate (↓ preload)
- Antiarrhythmic medications
  — Class I: Sodium channel blockers (reduce conduction velocity in the atria, ventricles, and His-Purkinje system)
    - IA
      □ Disopyramide (Norpace)
      □ Procainamide (Pronestyl)
      □ Quinidine
    - IB
      □ Lidocaine (Xylocaine)
      □ Mexiletine (Mexitil)
      □ Phenytoin (Dilantin)
      □ Tocainide (Tonocard)
    - IC
      □ Flecainide (Tambocor)
      □ Propafenone (Rythmol)
    - Other class I drugs
      □ Moricizine (Ethmozine)
  — Class II: β-adrenergic blockers (reduce automaticity of the SA node, decrease conduction velocity in the AV node)
    - Acebutolol (Sectral)
    - Atenolol (Tenormin)
    - Esmolol (Brevibloc)
    - Metoprolol (Lopressor)
    - Sotalol (Betapace)
  — Class III: Potassium channel blockers (delay repolarization)
    - Amiodarone (Cordarone)
    - Dofetilide (Tikosyn)
    - Sotalol (Betapace)

— Class IV: Calcium channel blockers (reduce automaticity of the SA node, delay AV node conduction)
  - Diltiazem (Cardizem)
  - Verapamil (Calan)
— Other antidysrhythmic drugs
  - Adenosine (Adenocard)
  - Digoxin (Lanoxin)
  - Ibutilide (Corvert)
  - Magnesium

Inflammatory Heart Disease

- Endocarditis
  — S/S: Fever, murmur, heart failure symptoms
  — Infective endocarditis can lead to damaged heart valves
  — Administer antibiotics for 4 to 6 weeks
  — Teach client about anticoagulant therapy
- Pericarditis
  — S/S: Pain—hurts more with deep breath, pericardial friction rub
  — Monitor for ST-segment elevation
  — Monitor hemodynamic status

Valvular Heart Disease

- Valves may be unable to:
  — Fully open (stenosis)
  — Fully close (insufficiency or regurgitation)
- Causes
  — Rheumatic fever
  — Congenital heart disease
  — Syphilis
  — Endocarditis
  — Hypertension

Mitral Valve Stenosis

- Early period—may be asymptomatic
- Later—excessive fatigue, dyspnea on exertion, orthopnea, dry cough, hemoptysis, or pulmonary edema
- Rumbling apical diastolic murmur and a-fib are common.

Nursing and Collaborative Management

- See section on heart failure
- Monitor for a-fib with thrombus formation
- Encourage prophylactic antibiotic therapy before any invasive procedures (dental, surgical, childbirth)
- Surgical repair or valve replacement may be required
  — With valve replacement: Teach the client about the need for lifelong anticoagulant therapy

Vascular Disorders
Arterial

- Smooth, shiny skin
- Pallor on elevation
- Weak peripheral pulses
- Sharp or tingling pain
- Cool to touch
- Intermittent claudication (classic symptom)
- Painful, nonedematous ulcers

52

Venous

- Monitor for history of deep vein thrombosis
- Bluish purple skin discoloration
- Normal peripheral pulses
- Warm to touch
- Slightly painful ulcers with marked edema

Nursing and Collaborative Management

General

- Change positions frequently; avoid sitting with crossed legs
- Wear NO restrictive clothing
- Keep extremities warm with clothing, not external heaters
- Discourage smoking
- With thrombosis: Administer thrombolytic agents

Arterial

- Bed rest
- Topical antibiotics
- Surgical intervention

Venous

- Systemic antibiotics
- Compression dressing
- Limb elevation

Abdominal Aortic Aneurysm

- Pulsating abdominal mass
- Bruit heard over abdomen
- Confirmed on x-ray study
- Rupture produces S/S of hypovolemic shock
- Postoperative care for surgical repair
  — Monitor for S/S of renal failure, postoperative ileus
  — Changes in pulses, S/S of occluded graft

Thrombophlebitis

- Inflammation of the venous wall with clot formation
- S/S: Calf pain, + Homans sign is a non-specific indicator, calf edema
- Restrict ambulation
- Elevate extremity
- Antiembolic stockings
- Medications
  — Heparin therapy
    • Monitor partial thromboplastin time (PTT)
  — Coumadin therapy
    • Monitor prothrombin time (PT), international normalized ratio (INR)
  — Antiplatelet agents
    • Ticlid
    • Plavix

Which client should the PN assess first?

A. A client receiving oxygen per nasal cannula who is dyspneic with mild exertion and has a hemoglobin of 7 g/dL

B. A client receiving IV aminoglycosides per CVC who complains of nausea and has a trough level below therapeutic levels

C. A client receiving packed RBCs who complains of flank pain and has a BP of 98/52 mm Hg

D. A client receiving chemotherapy who has a temperature of 98.9° F and a WBC count of 2,500/mm^3

Nursing and Collaborative Management

- Treatment of underlying pathology
- Administer blood products as ordered
- Diet should be high in iron-rich foods, folic acid, vitamin B_{12}, vitamin B_6, amino acids, and vitamin C
  — Parenteral iron is given using the z-track technique

HESI Test Question Approach			
Positive?		YES	NO
Key Words			
Rephrase			
Rule Out Choices			
A	B	C	D

6 Ingestion, Digestion, Absorption, and Elimination

The practical nurse is ordering afternoon snacks for several clients. The client who will benefit from a milkshake with whole milk and added protein powder has which condition?

A. Cirrhosis
B. Paralytic ileus
C. Cholelithiasis ~~kidney stone~~
D. Dumping syndrome

HESI Test Question Approach

Positive?		YES	NO
Key Words	Client will benefit		
Rephrase			
Rule Out Choices			
A	B	C	D

Gastroesophageal Reflux Disease (GERD)

- Not a disease but a syndrome
- Any clinically significant symptomatic condition secondary to reflux of gastric contents into the lower esophagus
- Most common upper GI problem seen in adults

There is no single cause of GERD.
- Predisposing conditions
  — Hiatal hernia
  — Incompetent lower esophageal sphincter (LES)
  — Decreased esophageal clearance (ability to clear liquids or food from the esophagus into the stomach)
  — Decreased gastric emptying

Nursing Assessment

- Heartburn after eating
- Fullness and discomfort after eating
- Ask client which foods seem to aggravate symptoms
- Positive diagnosis from barium swallow or fluoroscopy (hiatal hernia)

Nursing Plans and Interventions

- Encourage small, frequent meals
- Sit up while eating and remain upright for 1 hour after eating
- Stop eating 3 hours before bedtime
- Elevate head of bed 4 to 6 inches

Peptic Ulcer Disease

- Significant gastric ulcers are caused by *Helicobacter pylori* bacteria
- Risk factors
  — Medications—NSAIDs, corticosteroids
  — Alcohol
  — Cigarette smoking
  — Trauma

55

Nursing Assessment

- Left epigastric pain may radiate to back.
- Epigastric pain is relieved with food.
- Diagnostic procedures
  — Barium swallow
  — Upper endoscopy

Nursing Plans and Interventions

- When was the onset of symptoms?
- What relieves the symptoms?
- Monitor stools for color, consistency, occult blood.
- Administer antacids and antibiotics as ordered.
- Avoid caffeine.
- Small, frequent meals are best.

Complications

- Uncontrolled bleeding
  — Prepare for immediate surgery
- Dumping syndrome (postoperative complication)
  — Occurs 5 to 30 minutes after eating
  — Vertigo, syncope, tachycardia
  — Small, frequent meals
  — High-fat, high-protein, low-CHO diet
  — Avoid liquids with meals

Client Teaching

- Avoid medications such as:
  — Salicylates
  — NSAIDs
- Inform healthcare personnel of history of peptic ulcer disease
- Symptoms of GI bleeding
  — Dark, tarry stools
  — Coffee ground emesis
  — Bright red rectal bleeding

Lower GI Problems

Crohn's Disease

- Affects small and large intestines
- Right lower quadrant abdominal pain
- Nausea and vomiting
- Three to four stools per day
- Barium enema shows narrowing with areas of stricture separated by segments of normal bowel.

Interventions

- Initial treatment is based on symptomatic relief, which usually includes parenteral replacement of fluids, electrolytes, and blood products. Complete bed rest and assistance with ADLs during acute phases are prescribed.
- Pharmacotherapy
  — Sedatives and tranquilizers to promote rest and reduce anxiety
  — Antidiarrheal medications to decrease diarrhea and cramping
  — Sulfasalazine to treat acute exacerbations of colonic and ileocolonic disease

- Corticosteroids to reduce the active inflammatory response
- Immunosuppressive agents to allow dosage reduction or withdrawal of corticosteroids
- Antibiotics to control infections and perianal fistulas
- Nutritional management
  - During acute exacerbations, TPN and NPO
  - Elemental diet
  - Bland diets
  - No milk or milk products
  - Supplementation of vitamins and minerals, especially calcium, iron, folate, magnesium, vitamin D
- Surgical management is reserved for complications rather than used as a primary form of therapy. Common indications for surgery include bowel obstruction, internal and enterocutaneous fistulas, intraabdominal abscesses, and perianal disease.

Ulcerative Colitis
- Occurs in large bowel and rectum
- Symptoms
  - Diarrhea
  - Abdominal pain
  - Liquid stools, 10 to 20 per day
  - Anemia
- Interventions
  - Low-residue, low-fat, high-protein, high-calorie diet
  - No dairy products
  - Tepid fluids
  - Daily calorie count
  - Monitor I & O

Diverticular Diseases
- Left lower quadrant pain
- S/S of intestinal obstruction
  - Abdominal distention
  - Constipation/diarrhea
- + Barium enema
- Colonoscopy

Nursing Interventions
- High-fiber diet unless inflammation is present
- If inflammation is present:
  - NPO
  - Then low-residue, bland diet
  - Bulk-forming laxatives
  - Avoid heavy lifting, tight clothing, straining

Intestinal Obstruction
- Mechanical causes
  - Adhesions most common
  - Strangulated hernia
  - Tumors
- Neurogenic causes
  - Paralytic ileus
  - Spinal cord lesion
- Vascular cause
  - Mesenteric artery occlusion

57

Nursing Assessment
- Sudden abdominal pain
- History of obstruction
- High-pitched bowel sounds with early mechanical obstruction
- Bowel sounds diminished or absent with neurogenic or late mechanical obstruction

Nursing Interventions
- NPO
- IV fluids
- Nasogastric tube to intermittent suction

Liver, Pancreas, and Biliary Tract Problems

Cirrhosis
- Degeneration of the liver tissue
- Chronic, progressive disease

Nursing Assessment
- Early sign—RUQ pain
- History of alcohol and/or street drug abuse
- Jaundice
- Fruity or musty breath
- Asterixis — *floppy hand - cannot hold straight*
- Palmar erythema — *itchy hands*
- Ascites
- Weight loss

Esophageal Varices
- Esophageal varices may rupture.

Treatment
- Esophagogastric balloon
- Blakemore-Sengstaken tube
- Vitamin K — *helps clot*
- Blood products
- Coagulation factors

Nursing Interventions
- Monitor for bleeding
  - Avoid injections
  - Maintain pressure for 5 minutes after venipunctures
- Provide skin care
  - Avoid soap
  - Apply lotions
- Monitor fluid and electrolytes
  - Accurate I & O
  - Weigh daily
  - Restrict fluids (1,500 mL/day)
  - Abdominal girth

Dietary Teaching
- May need to restrict protein
- Low sodium
- Low potassium
- Low fat
- High carbohydrate
- May need to take lactulose (Cephulac) as ammonia detoxicant/stimulant laxative

Hepatitis

know route of transmission

Nursing Assessment

- Fatigue, weakness
- Anorexia, nausea
- Jaundice
- Dark urine
- Joint pain, muscle aches

Pancreatitis

- Acute: autodigestion of the pancreas
  — Alcohol ingestion and biliary tract disease are major causes.
- Chronic: Progressive, destructive disease
  — Long-term alcohol use is a major factor.

Acute Pancreatitis Assessment

Abdominal pain is the predominant symptom of acute pancreatitis.

- Located in the left upper quadrant
- Radiates to the back
- Sudden onset
- Described as severe, deep, piercing, and continuous
- Aggravated by eating and not relieved by vomiting
- Accompanied by flushing, cyanosis, and dyspnea

Avoid proteins. because they are harder to break down.

Other Manifestations of Acute Pancreatitis

- Nausea and vomiting
- Low-grade fever
- Jaundice
- Bowel sounds may be decreased or absent, and ileus may occur
- Areas of ecchymoses, *Grey Turner spots* (bluish flank discoloration), and *Cullen sign* (bluish periumbilical discoloration)
- Hypotension
- Tachycardia
- Hypovolemia (massive fluid shift into the retroperitoneal space)
- Shock (hemorrhage into the pancreas)
- The lungs are frequently involved (crackles)

"turns = side"
Grey Turner spots - Bluish discoloration on the flank
Cullen sign - Bluish discoloration around the belly.

Chronic Pancreatitis Assessment

- Steatorrhea - *fatty, ribbon-like, clay colored stool.*
- Diarrhea
- Jaundice
- Ascites
- Weight loss

Nursing Plans and Interventions

- Acute management
  — NPO
  — NG tube to suction
  — Morphine for pain management
  — Sitting up or leaning forward may reduce pain
  — Monitor blood sugar
  — Teach foods and fluids to avoid
- Chronic management
  — Pain management
    • Morphine

59

— Pancreatic enzymes
- Creon
- Viokase
- Mix powdered forms with fruit juice or apple-sauce; avoid mixing with proteins
- Teach foods and fluids to avoid

A client with an obstruction of the common bile duct caused by cholelithiasis passes clay-colored stools containing streaks of fat. What action should the practical nurse take?
A. Auscultate for diminished bowel sounds.
B. Send a stool specimen to the laboratory.
C. Document the assessment in the chart.
D. Notify the healthcare provider.

HESI Test Question Approach		
Positive?	**YES**	**NO**
Key Words		
Rephrase		
Rule Out Choices		
A	B	C	D

Cholecystitis and Cholelithiasis
- Cholecystitis—acute inflammation of the gallbladder
- Cholelithiasis—formation or presence of gallstones

Nursing Assessment
- Pain
- Fever
- Elevated WBC count
- Abdominal tenderness
- Jaundice

Nursing Plans and Interventions
- Analgesics for pain
- NPO
- NG to suction
- IV antibiotics
- Low-fat diet
  — Avoid fried, spicy, and fatty foods

Treatment
- Cholecystitis
  — IV hydration
  — Administer antibiotics
  — Pain management
- Cholelithiasis
  — Nonsurgical removal
    - Endoscopic retrograde cholangiopancreatography (ERCP)
    - Lithotripsy
  — Surgical approach
    - Cholecystectomy, laparoscopic or open

A client is admitted with gastric ulcer disease and GI bleeding. Which risk factor should the nurse identify in the client's history?

A. Eats heavily seasoned foods.
B. Uses NSAIDs daily.
C. Consumes alcohol every day.
D. Follows an acid-ash diet.

HESI Test Question Approach			
Positive?		YES	NO
Key Words	What		
Rephrase	What causes it?		
Rule Out Choices			
A	B	C	D

Renal and Urologic Problems

Urinary Tract Infections

- Obtain clean catch midstream specimen
- Administer antibiotics as ordered
  — Complete prescribed dose
  — Do not skip doses
- Encourage fluid intake of 3,000 mL/day
- Encourage voiding every 2 to 3 hours

Urinary Tract Obstruction

- Caused by calculi or stones
- Location of pain can help locate stone
  — Flank pain (stone usually in upper ureter)
  — Pain radiating to abdomen (stone likely in ureter or bladder)

Nursing Plans and Interventions

- Administer narcotics
- Strain all urine
- Encourage high fluid intake
  — 3 to 4 L per day
- Strict I & O
- Surgical management may be required

Benign Prostatic Hyperplasia

- Enlargement of the prostate
  — Most common treatment is transurethral resection of the prostate (TURP)
  — Can be done with laser to burn out prostate
  — If prostate is too large, use suprapubic approach
  — Assess for:
    • Increased urinary frequency/decreased output
    • Bladder distention (increases risk of spasm)

Nursing Plans and Interventions

- Preoperative teaching
  — Pain management
  — Oversized balloon catheter
- Bladder spasms
  — Common after surgery
  — Use antispasmodics
    • Belladonna and opium suppositories
    • Ditropan
    • Bentyl

- Continuous bladder irrigation is typically done to remove blood clots and ensure drainage
- Drainage should be reddish pink for 24 hours, clearing to light pink
- Monitor color and amount of urine output
- Notify physician if client has bright red bleeding with large clots

Discharge Teaching

- Continue to drink 12 to 14 glasses of water per day
- Avoid straining
- Avoid strenuous activity, sports, lifting, and intercourse for 3 to 4 weeks
- Report large amounts of blood or frank blood

A client who has acute renal failure is admitted to the hospital. The client's potassium level is 6.4 mEq/L. Which snack should the practical nurse offer?
A. Orange
B. Milkshake
C. Dried fruit and nuts
D. Gelatin dessert

HESI Test Question Approach			
Positive?		**YES**	**NO**
Key Words			
Rephrase			
Rule Out Choices			
A	**B**	**C**	**D**

Acute Renal Failure (ARF)

- A reversible syndrome if symptoms are caught early enough!
- Remember:
  — Kidneys use 25% of normal cardiac output to maintain function.
  — Kidneys excrete 1 to 2 L of urine per 24 hours for adults.
  — Three types of ARF
    • Prerenal
    • Intrarenal
    • Postrenal

Prerenal Failure

- Etiologic factors
  — Hemorrhage
  — Hypovolemia
  — Decreased cardiac output
  — Decreased renal perfusion

Intrarenal Failure

- Etiologic factors
  — May develop secondary to prerenal failure
  — Nephrotoxins
  — Infections (glomerulonephritis)
  — Renal injury
  — Vascular lesions

Postrenal Failure

- Etiologic factors for obstruction
  - Calculi
  - Benign prostatic hyperplasia (BPH)
  - Tumors
  - Strictures

Nursing Assessment

- Decreased urine output
- Weight gain
- Edema
- Diagnostic test results—Oliguric phase
  - ↓ Urine output
  - ↑ Blood urea nitrogen (BUN) and creatinine
  - ↑ Potassium
  - ↓ Sodium (serum)
  - ↓ pH
  - Metabolic acidosis
  - ↑ Urine sodium
  - Fixed at 1.010, specific gravity
- Diagnostic test results—Diuretic phase
  - ↑ Urine output
  - ↓ Fluid volume
  - ↓ Potassium
  - ↓ Sodium
  - ↓ Urine specific gravity
  - ↓ Urine sodium

Nursing Plans and Interventions

- In oliguric phase: Give only enough fluids to replace losses + 400 to 500 mL/24 hr
- Strict I & O
- Monitor laboratory values closely
- Watch for ECG changes
- Monitor weight daily

The nurse is evaluating the blood results for a client with end-stage renal disease who has just undergone hemodialysis. Which value should the nurse verify with the laboratory?

A. Elevated serum potassium
B. Increase in serum calcium
C. Low hemoglobin
D. Reduction in serum sodium

HESI Test Question Approach			
Positive?		YES	NO
Key Words			
Rephrase			
Rule Out Choices			
A	B	C	D

Chronic Kidney Disease (CKD)

- End-stage renal disease
- Progressive, irreversible damage to the nephrons and glomeruli
- Causes
  - Diabetic nephropathy
  - Hypertensive nephrosclerosis
  - Glomerulonephritis
  - Polycystic kidney disease

Nursing Assessment

- Early stage
  - Polyuria
  - Renal insufficiency
- Late stage
  - Oliguria
  - Hematuria
  - Proteinuria
  - Edema
  - Increased BP
  - Muscle wasting, secondary to negative nitrogen balance
  - Ammonia taste in mouth
  - ↑ Creatinine, ↑ phosphorus, ↑ potassium
- End stage
  - Anuria (<100 mL/24 hr)

Nursing Plans and Interventions

- Monitor serum electrolytes
- Weigh daily
- Strict I & O
- Renal diet
  - Low protein
  - Low sodium
  - Low potassium
  - Low phosphate

Medications

- Drugs to manage the associated complications
  - Aluminum hydroxide (to bind phosphates)
  - Epoetin (Epogen) (to treat anemia)
  - Antihypertensive therapy
  - Calcium supplements and vitamin D
  - Antihyperlipidemics
  - Statins (to lower LDL)
  - Fibrates (to lower triglycerides)
- CAUTION: As kidney function decreases, medication dosages must be adjusted.

Renal Dialysis

- Hemodialysis
  - AV fistula
- No venipunctures, IVs, or BP in AV shunt arm
- Withhold medications that would affect hemodynamic stability before dialysis
- Peritoneal dialysis
  - Monitor indwell and outflow times closely
  - Monitor I & O

Postoperative Care: Kidney Surgery

- Respiratory status
  - Auscultate to detect "wet" sounds
  - Demonstrate splinting method
- Circulatory status
  - Monitor for shock
  - Monitor surgical site for bleeding
- Pain relief status
  - Administer narcotic analgesics as needed
- Urinary status
  - Check urinary output and drainage from ALL tubes
  - Strict I & O

A male client who has type 1 diabetes returns to the clinic for follow-up after dietary counseling. The client states that he has been managing his diabetes closely. Which laboratory result indicates the client is maintaining tight control of the disease?

A. FBS changes from 135 to 110 mg/dL.
B. SMBG at HS changes from 45 to 90 mg/dL.
C. Glycosylated Hgb changes from 9% to 6%.
D. Urine ketones change from 0 to 3.

HESI Test Question Approach		
Positive?	YES	NO
Key Words		
Rephrase		
Rule Out Choices		
A	B	C	D

Obesity, Metabolic Syndrome, Prediabetes, and Diabetes

Primary Obesity

Primary obesity results when a person's calorie intake exceeds the body's metabolic rate.

- Assessed using a body mass index (BMI) chart
  - Normal weight: BMI = 18.5 to 24.9 kg/m^2
  - Overweight: BMI = 25 to 29.9 kg/m^2
  - Obese: BMI ≥ 30 kg/m^2
  - Morbidly obese: BMI > 40 kg/m^2
- Abdominal and visceral fat have been linked to metabolic syndrome
- Disproportionally represented in minority populations

Assessment

- Risk factor screening
  - Cardiovascular disease
  - Hypertension
  - Sleep apnea
  - Type 2 diabetes
  - Osteoarthritis

Nursing and Collaborative Management

- Lifestyle management
  - Medical nutritional therapy
  - Physical activity
  - Behavior modification
- Pharmacological therapy
- Bariatric surgery
  - Criteria for bariatric surgery
    - BMI ≥ 40 kg/m^2 *or*
    - BMI ≥ 35 kg/m^2 with one or more medical complications related to severe obesity
  - Gastric bypass, gastric banding, Roux-en-Y

Metabolic Syndrome

Metabolic syndrome is a collection of risk factors that increase an individual's chance of developing cardiovascular disease and diabetes mellitus.

Assessment

- The client meets three or more of the following criteria:
  - **Waist circumference**
    - Men: ≥40 inches (102 cm)
    - Women: ≥35 inches (88 cm)
  - **Triglycerides**
    - > 150 mg/dL *or*
    - Drug treatment for elevated triglycerides
  - **High-density lipoprotein (HDL) cholesterol**
    - Men: < 40 mg/dL
    - Women < 50 mg/dL *or*
    - Drug treatment for too-low HDL in either men or women
  - **BP**
    - ≥130 mm Hg systolic BP *or*
    - ≥85 mm Hg diastolic BP *or*
    - Drug treatment for hypertension
  - **Fasting blood glucose**
  - ≥110 mg/dL *or*
  - Drug treatment for elevated glucose

Nursing and Collaborative Management

- Lifestyle management

Prediabetes

Prediabetes is a condition in which individuals are at an increased risk of developing diabetes.

- Fasting blood glucose levels: 100 to 125 mg/dL
- 2-hour oral glucose tolerance test (OGTT): 140 to 199 mg/dL
- Hemoglobin A_{1C}: 5.7% to 6.4%

Diabetes Mellitus

Diabetes mellitus (DM) is a chronic, multisystem disease related to abnormal insulin production, impaired insulin utilization, or both.

- *Type 1 diabetes*: Immune-mediated disease; T cells attack and destroy beta cells, the source of insulin.
- *Type 2 diabetes*: The basic defect is insulin resistance; relative deficiency is more common than absolute deficiency. In the United States, 90-95% of persons with DM have type 2 DM.

Clinical Manifestations

- Type 1 DM
  - Rapid onset
  - Can occur at any age, but onset typically is seen in childhood or adolescence
  - Classic symptoms: Polyuria, polydipsia, polyphagia, weight loss
  - Weakness and fatigue also possible
  - Ketoacidosis may occur

- Type 2
  - Risk factors
    - Age > 45 years
    - BMI > 25
    - Family history of DM
    - Sedentary lifestyle
    - At-risk ethnic group
    - History of gestational diabetes
    - Cardiovascular co-morbidity
  - Onset is insidious with polyuria, polyphagia, polydipsia, and weight loss; the client may experience fatigue, recurrent infections, prolonged wound healing, blurred vision, impotence.
  - Development of ketoacidosis (rare).
  - A client with a blood glucose level > 600 mg/dL is likely to develop hyperosmolar hyperglycemia nonketotic syndrome (HHNKS).
- Other types of diabetes
  - Cystic fibrosis–related diabetes
  - Transplant-related diabetes
  - Gestational diabetes
  - Steroid-induced diabetes
  - Hospital-related hyperglycemia

Diagnostic Studies

Any of four tests can be used to diagnose type 1 or type 2 DM:

- HgbA$_{1C}$: >6.5%
- Fasting plasma glucose (FPG): ≥126 mg/dL
- 2-hour OGTT (75-g glucose load): 200 mg/dL
- Random blood glucose level > 200 mg/dL, accompanied by classic symptoms of hyperglycemia (polyuria, polydipsia, polyphagia, and unexplained weight loss)

Those in high-risk groups should have annual screening.

Nursing Assessment

- Integument: Skin breakdown
- Eyes: Retinal problems, cataracts
- Kidneys: Edema, urinary retention
- Periphery: Cool skin
- Ulcerations on extremities and thick nails
- Cardiopulmonary angina and dyspnea

Nursing and Collaborative Management

- Teach injection techniques
- Refrigerate unopened insulin
- Modify diet
  - 55% to 60% carbohydrate
  - 12% to 15% protein
  - 30% fat
- Physical activity
- Integrate meals and snacks, insulin therapy, and physical activity
- May need snack before or during exercise
- Monitor for S/S of hypoglycemia
- Foot care
  - Check feet daily
  - Report signs of injury

- Managing sick days
  - Keep taking insulin
  - Check blood sugar more frequently
  - Watch for S/S of hyperglycemia

The PN is assigned a client with diabetes. Which findings should the nurse report immediately?
A. Fingerstick blood sugar of 247 mg/dL
B. Diaphoresis and headache
C. Crackles at the end of inspiration
D. Numbness in the fingertips and toes

HESI Test Question Approach			
Positive?		YES	NO
Key Words			
Rephrase			
Rule Out Choices			
A	B	C	D

Oral Antidiabetic Agents

Oral antidiabetic agents are not insulin. These drugs work on the three defects of type 2 diabetes: (1) insulin resistance; (2) decreased insulin production; and (3) increased hepatic glucose production.

Types of Oral Antidiabetic Drugs
- *Sulfonylureas:* Increase insulin production from the pancreas; therefore, hypoglycemia is the major side effect.
  - Glipizide (Glucotrol, Glucotrol XL)
  - Glyburide (Micronase, DiaBeta, Glynase)
  - Glimepiride (Amaryl)
- *Meglitinides:* Increase insulin production from the pancreas; more rapidly absorbed and eliminated than sulfonylureas and therefore less likely to cause hypoglycemia.
  - Repaglinide (Prandin)
  - Nateglinide (Starlix)
- *Biguanides:* Reduce glucose production by the liver and enhance insulin sensitivity at the tissue level; the first-choice drug for most people with type 2 diabetes. Do not use in clients with kidney disease, liver disease, or heart failure or for clients who drink excessive amounts of alcohol.
  - Metformin (Glucophage)
- *α-Glucosidase inhibitors* (starch blockers): Slow the absorption of carbohydrate in the small intestine.
  - Acarbose (Precose)
  - Miglitol (Glyset)
- *Thiazolidinediones* (insulin sensitizers): Most effective for clients with insulin resistance; do not cause hypoglycemia when used alone.
  - Pioglitazone (Actos)
  - Rosiglitazone (Avandia)
    - Do not use in clients with heart failure because of increased risk of myocardial infarction and stroke.

69

- *Dipeptidyl peptidase-4 (DPP-4) inhibitors:* Inhibit DPP-4, slowing the inactivation of incretin hormones. Because DPP-4 inhibitors are glucose dependent, they lower the potential for hypoglycemia.
  — Sitagliptin (Januvia)
  — Saxagliptin (Onglyza)
- *Incretin mimetic:* Simulate one of the incretin hormones found to be decreased in people with type 2 diabetes. A prefilled pen is used to administer the drug subcutaneously. Acute pancreatitis and kidney problems have been associated with the use of these drugs.
  — Exenatide (Byetta)
  — Liraglutide (Victoza)
- *Amylin analog:* A synthetic analog of human amylin; indicated for clients with type 1 diabetes and for those with type 2 diabetes who have not achieved glucose control despite the use of insulin at mealtimes. This drug is administered subcutaneously and cannot be mixed with insulin; severe hypoglycemia can result if the drug is used with insulin.
  — Pramlintide (Symlin)

Insulin Pharmacokinetics after Subcutaneous Injection

- *Rapid-acting insulin:* Can be given IV.
  — Glulisine (Apidra)—given within 15 min of meal
    - Onset: 15 min
    - Peak: 1 hr
    - Duration: 2-3 hr
  — Lispro (Humalog)—given within 15 min of meal
    - Onset: 15 min
    - Peak: 1 hr
    - Duration: 4 hr
  — Aspart (NovoLog)—given within 15 min of meal
    - Onset: 30 min
    - Peak: 1-3 hr
    - Duration: 3-5 hr
  — Regular (Humulin R)—given within 30 min of meal
    - Onset: 30 min–1 hr
    - Peak: 2-4 hr
    - Duration: 5-7 hr
- *Intermediate-Acting Insulin:* Do not give IV; can be mixed with rapid-acting insulins (see Combinations section, below).
  — NPH
    - Onset: 3-4 hr
    - Peak: 6-12 hr
    - Duration: 18-28 hr
- *Long-Acting Insulin:* Cannot be mixed with any other type of insulin. Usually given once a day in the morning. Acts as basal insulin. Do not shake solutions. CAUTION: Solution is clear—do not confuse with regular insulin.
  — Glargine (Lantus)
    - Onset: 1-5 hr
    - Peak: Plateau
    - Duration: 24 hr
  — Detemir (Levemir)
    - Onset: 3-4 hr
    - Peak: Peakless
    - Duration: 24 hours

- **Combinations (Premix Insulins)**
  - NPH and regular: 70/30 (70% NPH insulin and 30% regular insulin)
    - Onset: 30 min–1 hr
    - Peak: 1.5-12 hr
    - Duration: Up to 24 hours
  - Lispro insulins: 75/25 (75% insulin lispro protamine suspension and 25% insulin lispro)
    - Onset: 15-30 min
    - Peak: ≥2 hr
    - Duration: About 22 hr
  - Lispro insulins: 50/50 (50% insulin lispro protamine suspension and 50% insulin lispro)
    - Onset: 15-30 min
    - Peak: 30-90 min
    - Duration: About 22 hr
  - Aspart insulins: 70/30 (70% insulin aspart protamine suspension and 30% insulin aspart)
    - Onset: About 10-20 min
    - Peak: 1-4 hr
    - Duration: Up to 24 hours
  - Because analog premixed insulin has a rapid onset, it should be given shortly before meals and should not be given at bedtime. Clients who choose to use premixed insulin preparations should have a fairly routine lifestyle.
- In clients with impaired liver or kidney function, the insulin dosage may need to be reduced, because insulin is metabolized by the liver and excreted by the kidneys.

Other Endocrine Problems

Which client should the practical nurse assess first?
A. The client with hyperthyroidism who has exophthalmos
B. The client with diabetes type 1 who has an inflamed foot ulcer
C. The client with Cushing's syndrome who has moon facies
D. The client with Addison's disease who has tremors and diaphoresis

Thyroid Gland Feedback Loop
Hypothalamus

TRH (+)

Anterior pituitary

— T_3 and T_4 (−) TSH (+)

— Thyroid gland

Hyperthyroidism
Nursing Assessment
- Enlarged thyroid gland
- Exophthalmos
- Weight loss

HESI Test Question Approach			
Positive?		YES	NO
Key Words			
Rephrase			
Rule Out Choices			
A	B	C	D

- Elevated T_3
- Elevated T_4
- Diarrhea
- Tachycardia
- Bruit over thyroid

Nursing Plans and Interventions
- Diet—high protein, high calorie, low caffeine, low fiber
- Treatment may trigger hypothyroidism; client may need hormone replacement.
- Propylthiouracil (PTU) therapy to block the synthesis of T_3 and T_4
- Iodine (^{131}I) therapy to destroy thyroid cells

Surgical Management
- Thyroidectomy
- Check behind neck for drainage
- Support neck when moving client
- Assess for laryngeal edema
- Have trach set, oxygen, and suction equipment at bedside
- Have calcium gluconate at bedside

Hypothyroidism
- Fatigue
- Bradycardia
- Weight gain
- Constipation
- Periorbital edema
- Cold intolerance
- Low T_3 (<70 ng/dL)
- Low T_4 (<5 ng/dL)

Nursing Plans and Interventions
- Be alert for myxedema coma, an acute exacerbation of hypothyroidism.
- Maintain airway!
- Teach medication regimen.
- Monitor for side effects of medications.
- Monitor bowel program for S/S of constipation.

Thyroid Preparations
- Levothyroxine (Synthroid)
  — Monitor heart rate
  — Hold for pulse > 100 beats/min
- Liothyronine (Cytomel)
  — Increases metabolic rate
  — Acts as synthetic T_3
  — Check hormone levels regularly
  — Avoid food containing iodine
- Levothyroxine (T_4) + liothyronine (T_3) (Liotrix)
  — Rapid onset

Addison's Disease
Etiology
- Sudden withdrawal from corticosteroids
- Hypofunction of adrenal cortex
- Lack of pituitary ACTH

Signs and Symptoms
- Weight loss
- N/V
- Hypovolemia
- Hypoglycemia
- Hyponatremia
- Hyperkalemia
- Loss of body hair
- Postural hypotension
- Hyperpigmentation

Nursing Plans and Interventions
- Frequent vital signs
- Weigh daily
- Monitor serum electrolytes
- Diet
  — High sodium
  — Low potassium
  — High carbohydrate
- Encourage client to drink at least 3 L of fluid per day

Cushing's Syndrome
Cushing's syndrome results from excess adrenocorticoid activity, which is caused by a tumor or tumors of the adrenals or the pituitary or hypothalamus gland.

Nursing Assessment
- Moon face and edema of lower extremities
- Flat affect
- Obesity with abdominal striae
- Buffalo hump (fat deposits)
- Muscle atrophy, weakness
- Dry, pale, thin skin
- Hypertension
- Osteoporosis
- Immunosuppressed
- Hypovolemic
- Hirsutism
- Laboratory results
  — Hyperglycemia
  — Hypercalcemia
  — Hypernatremia
  — Hypokalemia
  — Increased plasma cortisol levels

Nursing Plans and Interventions
- Monitor for S/S of infection
  — Fever
  — Skin lesions
  — Elevated WBCs
- Diet
  — Low sodium
  — Low carbohydrate

The client at the assisted living facility is prescribed prednisone 10 mg orally daily. The PN reinforces teaching for the client about the medication. Which statement by the client indicates that further teaching is necessary?

A. "I can take aspirin if I need it for pain."
B. "I need to take the medication at the same time daily."
C. "I need to check for bruising on my skin."
D. "If I gain more than 5 pounds a week, I will call my doctor."

HESI Test Question Approach			
Positive?		YES	NO
Key Words			
Rephrase			
Rule Out Choices			
A	B	C	D

Sexually Transmitted Diseases (STDs)

- Symptoms and treatment
  — Vary by disease
- Teach safe sex
  — Limit number of partners
  — Use latex condoms
- Report incidence of STDs to appropriate health agencies

Refer to Review Manuals for more in-depth information about STDs:

- *Evolve Reach Comprehensive Review for the NCLEX-RN Examination (powered by HESI)*
- *Mosby's Comprehensive Review of Nursing for the NCLEX-RN Examination*
- *Saunders Comprehensive Review for the NCLEX-RN Examination*

Female Reproductive Problems

A 52-year-old client who had had an abdominal hysterectomy because of a grade III (severe dysplasia) Pap smear result is preparing for discharge. Which recommendation should the PN offer the client about women's health and screening exams?

A. "Continue your annual Pap smear, mammogram, clinical breast exam, and monthly breast self-exam (BSE)."
B. "A Pap smear is no longer necessary, but continue your annual mammogram and clinical breast exam, plus monthly BSE."
C. "When the ovaries have been removed, only an annual mammogram and clinical breast exam are necessary."
D. "Annual mammograms are not necessary if biannual clinical breast exams and weekly BSE are done."

HESI Test Question Approach			
Positive?		YES	NO
Key Words			
Rephrase			
Rule Out Choices			
A	B	C	D

Benign Uterine Tumors

- Arise from muscle tissue of the uterus
- Signs and symptoms
  — Menorrhagia
  — Uterine enlargement
  — Dysmenorrhea
  — Anemia secondary to menorrhagia
  — Uterine enlargement

— Low back pain and pelvic pain
— Tend to disappear after menopause
■ Surgical options
— Myomectomy
— Hysterectomy
■ Fertility issues

A 76-year-old client reports that since she stopped hormone replacement therapy (HRT), she has had increased vaginal discomfort during intercourse. What action should the nurse take?
A. Suggest that the client use a vaginal cream or lubricant
B. Recommend that the client abstain from sexual intercourse
C. Teach the client Kegel exercises daily
D. Instruct the client to resume HRT

HESI Test Question Approach			
Positive?		**YES**	**NO**
Key Words			
Rephrase			
Rule Out Choices			
A	B	C	D

Uterine Prolapse, Cystocele, and Rectocele
Preventive Measures
— Postpartum perineal (Kegel) exercises
— Spaced pregnancies
— Weight control
■ Different S/S for each condition
■ Surgical intervention
— Hysterectomy
— Anterior and posterior vaginal repair

Nursing Interventions
■ Postoperative pain management
■ Monitor postoperative urinary output
■ Observe for postoperative S/S of bleeding and infection

A client who had a vaginal hysterectomy the previous day is saturating perineal pads with blood and requires frequent changes during the night. What priority action should the nurse take?
A. Provide iron-rich foods on each dietary tray
B. Monitor the client's vital signs every 2 hours
C. Administer IV fluids at the prescribed rate
D. Encourage postoperative leg exercises

HESI Test Question Approach			
Positive?		**YES**	**NO**
Key Words			
Rephrase			
Rule Out Choices			
A	B	C	D

Male Reproductive Problems

Etiology and Pathophysiology
Prostatitis is one of the most common urological disorders. The four categories of prostatitis syndromes are:
■ Acute bacterial prostatitis
■ Chronic bacterial prostatitis
■ Chronic prostatitis/chronic pelvic pain syndrome
■ Asymptomatic inflammatory prostatitis

Common manifestations of acute bacterial prostatitis include:

- Fever and chills
- Back pain
- Perineal pain
- Dysuria
- Urinary frequency
- Urgency
- Cloudy urine

Diagnostic Studies

- Urinalysis (UA)
- Urine culture
- White blood cells (WBCs)
- Blood cultures
- PSA test

Management

- Antibiotics
  — Trimethoprim/sulfamethoxazole (Bactrim)
  — Ciprofloxacin (Cipro)
  — Ofloxacin (Floxin)
  — Doxycycline (Vibramycin)
  — Tetracycline
- Antiinflammatory agents for pain control

Nursing interventions

- Encourage fluid intake

Problems of Erectile Mechanism

Priapism is a painful erection that lasts longer than 6 hours. It is caused by obstruction of the venous outflow in the penis. The condition may be a medical emergency.

Causes

- Thrombosis of the veins of the corpora cavernosa
- Leukemia
- Sickle cell anemia
- Diabetes mellitus
- Degenerative lesions of the spine
- Neoplasms of the brain or spinal cord

Treatment

- Sedatives
- Injection of smooth muscle relaxants directly into the penis
- Aspiration and irrigation of the corpora cavernosa with a large-bore needle
- Shunt to drain the corpora

Complications include penile tissue necrosis.

Sexual Functioning

Vasectomy is the bilateral surgical ligation of the vas deferens, performed for the purpose of sterilization.

Erectile dysfunction (ED) is the inability to attain or maintain an erect penis to allow satisfactory sexual performance. ED is increasing in all segments of the

76

sexually active male population. ED can result from a number of factors, including:

- Diabetes
- Vascular disease
- Side effects of medications
- Result of surgery (prostatectomy)
- Trauma
- Chronic illness
- Decreased gonadal hormone secretion
- Stress
- Depression
- Vascular disease (most common cause)

The treatment for ED is based on the underlying cause.

Oral Drug Therapy

- Sildenafil (Viagra)
- Tadalafil (Cialis)
- Vardenafil (Levitra)

8 Movement, Coordination, and Sensory Input

The practical nurse initiates neuro checks for a client at risk for neurological compromise. Which manifestation typically provides the first indication of altered neurological function?

A. Change in level of consciousness
B. Increasing muscular weakness
C. Changes in pupil size bilaterally
D. Progressive nuchal rigidity

HESI Test Question Approach			
Positive?		YES	NO
Key Words			
Rephrase			
Rule Out Choices			
A	B	C	D

Altered State of Consciousness

Glasgow Coma Scale

- Used to assess level of consciousness (LOC)
- Score: maximum, 15; minimum, 3
  - ≤ 7 = Coma
  - 3-4 = High mortality rate
  - >8 = Good prognosis
- A decrease in LOC may be the earliest sign of increasing ICP.

Table 8-1 Glasgow Coma Scale*

Eye Opening	
Spontaneous	4
To sound	3
To pain	2
Never	1
Motor Response	
Obeys commands	6
Localizes pain	5
Normal flexion (withdrawal)	4
Abnormal flexion	3
Extension	2
None	1
Verbal Response	
Oriented	5
Confused conversation	4
Inappropriate words	3
Incomprehensible sounds	2
None	1

*The highest possible score is 15
(Ignatavicius 917)
Ignatavicius, Workman. *Medical-Surgical Nursing: Patient-Centered Collaborative Care, 7th Edition.* W.B. Saunders Company, 2013.

- Neurological vital signs
  — Pupil size (with sizing scale)
  — Limb movement (with scale)
  — Vital signs (blood pressure, temperature, pulse, respirations)

Nursing Assessment
- Assess for early S/S of changes in LOC
  — Decreasing LOC
  — Change in orientation
- Late signs
  — Cushing's triad
    • Widening pulse pressure
    • Slowing heart rate
    • Slowing respirations
  — Change in size, response of pupils; dilated on side of injury initially
  — Elevated temperature
  — Posturing
- Assess for change in respiratory status
  — Cheyne-Stokes respiration

Nursing and Collaborative Management for Increased ICP
- Maintain airway and provide adequate oxygenation
  — Mechanical ventilation possible with ↓ LOC
  — Hyperventilate before suctioning
  — Limit suctioning to 15 seconds
  — Keep airway free of secretions
  — Prevent aspiration
- Prevent complications related to sustained ↑ ICP
  — ICP monitoring target: 5-15 mmHg
  — Elevate head of bed to 30 to 45 degrees to promote venous return
  — Place the neck in a neutral position (not flexed or extended) to promote venous drainage
  — Position client to avoid flexion of the hips, waist, and neck and rotation of the head, especially to the right
  — Implement measures to help client avoid Valsalva maneuver

Medications
- Hyperosmotic agents
  — 20% Mannitol
  — Steroids
    • Decadron
    • Solu-Medrol
  — Barbiturates
- Prophylactic phenytoin (Dilantin)
- Diuretics
- Alternate with mannitol
- Avoid narcotics

Which change in the status of a client being treated for increased ICP warrants immediate action by the practical nurse?
A. Urinary output increases from 20 to 50 mL/hr
B. Arterial Po_2 increases from 80 to 90 mm Hg
C. Glasgow Coma Scale score changes from 5 to 7
D. Pulse drops from 88 to 68 beats/min

HESI Test Question Approach			
Positive?		YES	NO
Key Words			
Rephrase			
Rule Out Choices			
A	B	C	D

Head Injury

Assessment

- Changes in LOC
- Signs of increased ICP
  — Changes in VS
  — Headache
  — Vomiting
  — Pupillary changes
  — Seizure
  — Ataxia
  — Abnormal posturing (decerebrate or decorticate)

CSF Leakage

- Risk of meningitis with leakage
- Usual signs of increased ICP may not be seen with CSF leakage
- Drainage may come from nose (rhinorrhea) or ears (otorrhea)

Nursing Interventions

- Neurological assessment every 15 min
- Notify healthcare provider at FIRST sign of deterioration
- Limit visitors
- Keep room quiet
- Prevent straining
- Keep HOB at 30 to 45 degrees
- Avoid neck flexion/straining
- Monitor I & O

The nurse is planning a class on stroke prevention for clients with hypertension. What information is most important to provide the clients in the class?
A. Salt restriction diet
B. Weight reduction
C. Medication compliance
D. Risk for stroke

HESI Test Question Approach			
Positive?		YES	NO
Key Words			
Rephrase			
Rule Out Choices			
A	B	C	D

Stroke (Brain Attack) or Cerebrovascular Accident

- Hemorrhage into brain tissue
- Ischemic clot
  — Thrombotic
  — Embolic
- Transient ischemic attack (TIA)
  — Temporary episode of neurological dysfunction lasting less than 24 hours and often less than 15 minutes.

Nursing and Collaborative Management

- Time lost is brain lost
- Hemorrhagic or ischemic
- CT scan or MRI
- Prepare for thrombolytic (limited therapeutic window)
- Assess for S/S of increased ICP
- Assess verbal ability and plan care appropriate to client's ability to communicate
- Assess swallowing to prevent aspiration
- Assess for bowel and bladder control
- Assess functional abilities
  — Mobility
  — Activities of daily living (ADLs)
  — Elimination

A client with Parkinson's disease is prescribed carbidopa-levodopa (Sinemet). Which observation by the PN indicates that the desired effect of the medication is being achieved?
A. Decreased blood pressure
B. Steady gait
C. Increased salivation
D. Increased attention span

Parkinson's Disease

- Triad of symptoms
  — Rigidity
    • Masklike face
  — Akinesia
    • Difficulty initiating and continuing movement
  — Tremors
    • Resting tremors
    • Pill rolling

Nursing Plans and Interventions

- SAFETY is always a priority!
- Take medications with meals
- Change positions slowly to reduce postural hypotension
- Thicken liquids
- Soft, ground foods
- Encourage activity and exercise

HESI Test Question Approach			
Positive?		**YES**	**NO**
Key Words			
Rephrase			
Rule Out Choices			
A	B	C	D

Medications

- ■ *Dopaminergics*
  - — Levodopa (L-dopa, dopamine)
    - • Blocks breakdown of levodopa to allow more levodopa to cross the blood-brain barrier
    - • Avoid foods high in vitamin B6 and high-protein foods
  - — Levodopa-carbidopa (Sinemet, Paracopa [orally dissolving tablet])
    - • Allows for less use of levodopa and helps decrease side effects
  - — Bromocriptine mesylate (Parlodel)
    - • Helps with motor fluctuations
  - — Pergolide (Permax)
  - — Pramipexole (Mirapex)
  - — Ropinirole (Requip)
  - — Amantadine (Symmetrel)
  - — Apomorphine (Apokyn)
- ■ *Anticholinergics*—to treat tremors
  - — Trihexyphenidyl (Artane)
  - — Benztropine (Cogentin)
  - — Biperiden (Akineton)
- ■ *Antihistamine*
  - — Diphenhydramine (Benadryl)
- ■ *Monoamine oxidase inhibitors*—slows disease progression
  - — Selegiline (Eldepryl, Carbex)
  - — Rasagiline (Azilect)
- ■ *Catechol-O-methyl transferase* (COMT) inhibitors—may help preserve dopaminergic levels
  - — Entacapone (Comtan)
  - — Tolcapone (Tasmar)

Guillain-Barré Syndrome

- ■ Usually occurs after upper respiratory infection
- ■ Ascending paralysis
- ■ Rapid demyelination of nerves
- ■ Paralysis of respiratory system may occur quickly
- ■ Prepare to intubate

Treatment

- ■ Plasmapheresis over 10 to 15 days
- ■ IV high-dose immunoglobulin (Sandoglobulin) is as effective as plasma exchange and has the advantage of immediate availability and greater safety; clients receiving high-dose immunoglobulin must be well hydrated and have adequate renal function.
- ■ Maintain patent airway
- ■ Reposition frequently
- ■ Impaired swallowing may require TPN
- ■ Supervise feedings

Multiple Sclerosis (MS)

- ■ Demyelination of the central nervous system (CNS) myelin
- ■ Messages garbled; short-circuited from brain to CNS
- ■ Disease characterized by periods of remission and exacerbation

- Assessment findings
  — Changes in visual field
  — Weaknesses in extremities
  — Numbness
  — Visual or swallowing difficulties
  — Unusual fatigue
  — Gait disturbances

Nursing Interventions
- Keep objects labeled
- Avoid quick changes in room lighting
- Provide assistive devices
- Thicken liquids

Medication Management
Focuses on controlling symptoms.
- *Corticosteroids*
  — ACTH, prednisone, methylprednisolone
- *Immunomodulators*
  — Interferon beta (Betaseron, Avonex, Rebif)
  — Glatiramer acetate (Copaxone)
- *Immunosuppressants*
  — Mitoxantrone (Novantrone)
- *Cholinergics*
  — Bethanechol (Urecholine)
  — Neostigmine (Prostigmin)
- *Anticholinergics*
  — Propantheline (Pro-Banthine)
  — Oxybutynin (Ditropan)
- *Muscle relaxants*
  — Diazepam (Valium)
  — Baclofen (Lioresal)
  — Dantrolene (Dantrium)
  — Tizanidine (Zanaflex)
- *CNS stimulants*
  — Pemoline (Cylert)
  — Methylphenidate (Ritalin)
  — Modafinil (Provigil)
- *Antiviral/antiparkinsonian drugs*
  — Symmetrel (Amantadine)

Myasthenia Gravis
- Chronic neuromuscular autoimmune disease
- Causes weakness and abnormal fatigue of voluntary muscles

Nursing Assessment
- Ocular muscle weakness
- Bulbar muscle weakness
- Skeletal muscle weakness

Diagnosis
- Based on clinical presentation
  — Muscle weakness
- Confirmed by testing response to anticholinesterase drugs
- Tensilon test—2 mg IV

Medications

- *Anticholinesterase agents*
  — Try to achieve maximum strength and endurance
  — Block action of cholinesterase
  — Increase levels of ACh at junctions
  — Common medications
    - Mestinon
    - Prostigmin
  — Start with minimal doses
  — Onset: 30 min
  — Duration: 3 to 4 hr
  — Must take on time!
- *Corticosteroids*
  — Prednisone
- *Immunosuppressants*
  — Azathioprine (Imuran)
  — Cyclophosphamide (Cytoxan)

Types of Crisis

- Myasthenic
  — MEDICAL EMERGENCY!
  — Caused by undermedication or infection
  — Positive Tensilon test
  — Changes in VS, cyanosis, loss of cough and gag reflex, incontinence
  — May require intubation
- Cholinergic
  — Results from overmedication
  — Toxic levels of anticholinesterase medications
  — Symptoms—abdominal cramps, diarrhea, excessive pulmonary secretions
  — Negative Tensilon test

Nursing Interventions

- Coughing and deep-breathing exercises
- Suction equipment at bedside
- Sit upright when eating and for 1 hour afterward
- Keep chin downward when swallowing
- Plan activities carefully; weakness is greater at the end of the day

Spinal Cord Injury

- Injuries classified by:
  — Extent of injury
  — Level of injury
  — Mechanism of injury
- Injuries classified as complete or incomplete
  — Transection/partial transection
- Rule of thumb
  — Injury above C8 = quadriplegic
  — Injury below C8 = paraplegic

Nursing Assessment

- Start with ABCs
- Determine quality of respiratory status
- Check neurological status
- Assess vital signs
- Hypotension and bradycardia occur with injuries above T6

Nursing Plans and Interventions

- Immobilize and stabilize!
- Keep neck and body in anatomical alignment
- Maintain patent airway
- Clients with cervical injuries are placed in skeletal traction
- High-dose corticosteroids are used to control edema during first 24 hours
- Spinal shock
- Flaccid paralysis
  - Complete loss of reflexes
  - Hypotension
  - Bradycardia
  - Bowel and bladder distention
  - Reverse as quickly as possible

Autonomic Dysreflexia

- Medical emergency that occurs in clients with injuries at or above T6
- Exaggerated autonomic reflex response
- Usually triggered by bowel or bladder distention
- S/S—severe headache, ↑ BP, bradycardia, profuse sweating
- Elevate head of bed (while maintaining correct alignment); relieve bowel or bladder distention

Rehabilitation

- Watch for paralytic ileus
  - Assess bowel sounds
- Kinetic bed to promote blood flow
- Antiembolic stockings
- Protect from skin breakdown
- Bowel and bladder training
  - Keeping bladder empty and urine dilute and acidic to help prevent urinary tract infection, a common cause of death after spinal cord injury

Which action by the unlicensed assistive personnel (UAP) requires immediate follow-up by the nurse?

A. Positions a client who is 12 hours post above-the-knee amputation (AKA) with the residual limb elevated on a pillow
B. Assists a client with ambulation while the client uses a cane on the unaffected side
C. Accompanies a client who has lupus erythematosus to sit outside in the sun during a break
D. Helps a client with rheumatoid arthritis to the bathroom after the client takes Celebrex

Fractures
Signs and Symptoms

- Pain, swelling, deformity of the extremity
- Discoloration, loss of functional ability
- Fracture evident on x-ray study

HESI Test Question Approach			
Positive?		YES	NO
Key Words			
Rephrase			
Rule Out Choices			
A	B	C	D

Nursing Plans and Interventions

- Instruct client on proper use of assistive devices
- Assess for 5Ps of neurovascular functioning
  — Pain
  — Paresthesia
  — Pulse
  — Pallor
  — Paralysis
- Assess neurovascular area distal to injury
  — Skin color, temperature, sensation, capillary refill, mobility, pain, pulses

Treatment

- Closed reduction
- Open reduction
- Postreduction
  — Cast
  — Traction
  — External fixation
  — Splints
  — Orthoses (braces)

An adult client with a fracture of the femur is being discharged from the fast track clinic after application of a plaster cast. The PN should reinforce with the client the need to use which method to dry the cast over the next 24 hours?
A. Place plastic wrap on the bottom of the cast
B. Support the cast on a firm surface during the night
C. Keep the cast's surfaces exposed to circulating air
D. Use a blow dryer set at low for 10 minutes every hour × 4.

HESI Test Question Approach		
Positive?	YES	NO
Key Words		
Rephrase		
Rule Out Choices		
A	B	C	D

Joint Replacement

- After surgery
  — Check circulation, sensation, and movement of extremity distal to replacement area
  — Keep body in proper alignment
  — Encourage fluid intake
  — Have client use bedpan, commode chair
  — Coordinate rehabilitation process
- Discharge home
  — Safety
  — Accessibility
- Drugs
  — Anticoagulants
  — Analgesics
  — Parenteral antibiotics

Amputation

- Postoperative care
  — Monitor surgical dressing for drainage
  — Ensure proper body alignment
  — Elevate residual limb (stump) for first 24 hours
  — Do NOT elevate after 48 hours

— Provide passive range of motion (ROM) and encourage prone position periodically to reduce risk of contracture
— Perform proper stump bandaging to prepare for prosthesis
— Coordinate care with OT and PT
— Remember—phantom limb pain is real and requires pharmacological interventions

A postmenopausal woman who has a BMI of 18 is at the clinic for her annual well woman examination. Which teaching plan topic should the nurse prepare for this high-risk client?
A. Osteoporosis
B. Obesity
C. Anorexia
D. Breast cancer

HESI Test Question Approach

Positive?		YES	NO
Key Words			
Rephrase			
Rule Out Choices			
A	B	C	D

Osteoporosis
Risk Factors

- Small, postmenopausal females
- Diet low in calcium
- Excessive use of alcohol, tobacco, and caffeine
- Inactive lifestyle
- Men: Low testosterone level

Nursing Assessment

- Dowager hump
- Kyphosis of the dorsal spine
- Loss of height
- Pathological fractures
- Compression fracture of spine can occur

Nursing and Collaborative Management

- Keep bed in low position
- Provide adequate lighting
- Avoid using throw rugs
- Provide assistance with ambulation
- Follow regular exercise program
- Diet high in vitamin D, protein, and calcium

Osteoporosis Drug Therapy

- *Bisphosphonates*
  - Alendronate (Fosamax)
  - Clodronate (Bonefos)
  - Etidronate (Didronel)
  - Ibandronate (Boniva)
  - Pamidronate (Aredia)
  - Risedronate (Actonel)
  - Tiludronate (Skelid)
- *Selective estrogen receptor modulators*
  - Raloxifene (Evista)
  - Teriparatide (Forteo)

Rheumatoid Arthritis

- Chronic, systemic, progressive deterioration of connective tissue
- Etiology unknown; believed to be autoimmune

Nursing Assessment

- Young to middle age
- More females than males
- Systemic, with exacerbations and remissions
- Affects small joints first, then spreads
- Stiffness (may decrease with use)
- Decreased range of motion
- Joint pain
- Elevated erythrocyte sedimentation rate (ESR)
- Positive rheumatoid factor (RF) in 80% of clients
- Narrowed joint space

Nursing and Collaborative Management
Drug Therapy

- High-dose ASA or NSAIDs
- Systemic corticosteroids
- Disease-modifying antirheumatic drugs
  — Methotrexate (Rheumatrex)
  — Sulfasalazine (Azulfidine)
  — Hydroxychloroquine (Plaquenil)
  — Leflunomide (Arava)
- Heat and cold applications
- Weight management
- Rest and joint protection
- Assistive devices
- Shower chair
- Canes, walkers
- Straight-backed chairs, elevated seats

Lupus Erythematosus

- Discoid lupus erythematosus (DLE)—affects skin only
- Systemic lupus erythematosus (SLE)—more prevalent than DLE
- Major trigger factors
  — Sunlight
  — Infectious agents
  — Stress
  — Drugs
  — Pregnancy

Nursing Assessment

- DLE—scaly rash, butterfly rash over bridge of nose
- SLE—joint pain, fever, nephritis, pericarditis (Figure 8-1)
- Photosensitivity

Nursing and Collaborative Management

- Teaching
  — Drugs
  — Pain management
  — Disease process
  — Conservation of energy
  — Avoid exposure to ultraviolet rays

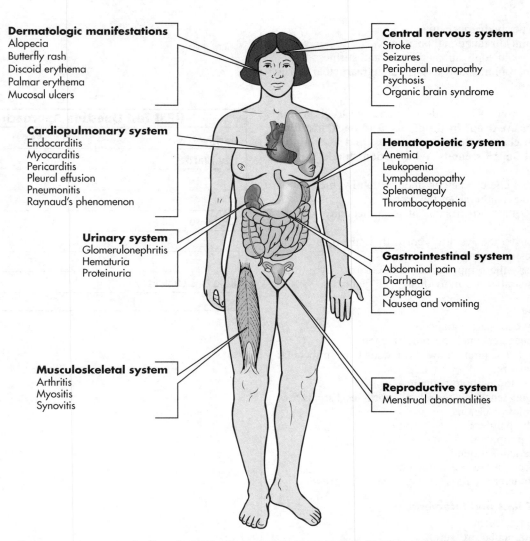

Dermatologic manifestations
Alopecia
Butterfly rash
Discoid erythema
Palmar erythema
Mucosal ulcers

Central nervous system
Stroke
Seizures
Peripheral neuropathy
Psychosis
Organic brain syndrome

Cardiopulmonary system
Endocarditis
Myocarditis
Pericarditis
Pleural effusion
Pneumonitis
Raynaud's phenomenon

Hematopoietic system
Anemia
Leukopenia
Lymphadenopathy
Splenomegaly
Thrombocytopenia

Urinary system
Glomerulonephritis
Hematuria
Proteinuria

Gastrointestinal system
Abdominal pain
Diarrhea
Dysphagia
Nausea and vomiting

Musculoskeletal system
Arthritis
Myositis
Synovitis

Reproductive system
Menstrual abnormalities

Figure 8-1 Common assessment findings in SLE. (From Lewis S, Dirksen S, Heitkemper M et al: *Medical-surgical nursing: Assessment and management of clinical problems,* ed 5, St Louis, 2010, Mosby.)

— Avoid/reduce stress
— Use mild soaps, creams for skin care
— Use of steroids for joint inflammation
■ Therapeutic exercise and heat therapy
■ Marital and pregnancy counseling

Degenerative Joint Disease (Osteoarthritis)
■ Joint pain increases with activity
■ Morning stiffness
■ Crepitus
■ Limited movement
■ Joint enlargement

Nursing and Collaborative Management
■ Follow weight-reduction diet
■ Excessive use of involved joint may accelerate degeneration

- Use proper body mechanics
- Keep joints in functional position
- Hot and cold applications for pain and stiffness
- NSAIDs, opioid analgesics, and intraarticular corticosteroids

The PN observes an elderly client with glaucoma administer eye drops by tilting his head back, instilling each drop close to the inner canthus, and keeping his eye closed for 15 seconds. What action should the PN take first?

A. Ask the client whether another family member is available to administer the drops

B. Review the correct steps of the procedure with the client

C. Administer the eye drops correctly in the other eye to demonstrate the technique

D. Discuss the importance of correct eye drop administration for individuals with glaucoma

Glaucoma

- Primary open-angle glaucoma
  - Drainage channels become clogged
  - Aqueous humor flow is reduced in trabecular meshwork
- Primary closed-angle glaucoma
  - Bulging lens from age related processes disrupts flow
- Silent thief of vision
- Normally painless
- Loss of peripheral vision
- May see halos around lights
- Diagnosed with eye examination
  - Tonometer used to measure intraocular pressure

Nursing Plans and Interventions

- Keys to treatment
  - ↓ Intraocular pressure
  - ↓ Aqueous humor production
  - ↑ Drainage of aqueous humor
  - Teach client and family proper eye drop instillation
  - Teach client how to avoid activities that can increase intraocular pressure

Nursing Management and Collaborative Therapy

- Ambulatory/home care for open-angle glaucoma
  - Drug therapy
    - β-Adrenergic blockers
    - α-Adrenergic agonists
    - Cholinergic agents
    - Carbonic anhydrase inhibitors
  - Surgical options
    - Argon laser trabeculoplasty
    - Trabeculectomy with or without filtering implant
- Acute care for closed-angle glaucoma
  - Topical cholinergic agent
  - Hyperosmotic agent
  - Laser peripheral iridotomy
  - Surgical iridectomy

HESI Test Question Approach			
Positive?		YES	NO
Key Words			
Rephrase			
Rule Out Choices			
A	B	C	D

Glaucoma Drug Therapy

- *β-Adrenergic blockers*
  — Betaxolol (Betoptic)
  — Levobunolol (Betagan)
  — Metipranolol (OptiPranolol)
  — Timolol maleate (Timoptic, Istalol)
- *α-Adrenergic agonists*
  — Dipivefrin (Propine)
  — Epinephrine (Epifrin, Eppy, Gaucon, Epitrate, Epinal, Eppy/N)
  — Apraclonidine (Lopidine)
  — Brimonidine (Alphagan)
  — Latanoprost (Xalatan)
- *Cholinergic agents (miotics)*
  — Carbachol (Isopto Carbachol)
  — Pilocarpine (Akarpine; Isopto-Carpine, Pilocar, Pilopine, Piloptic, Pilostat)
- *Carbonic anhydrase inhibitors*
  — Systemic
    • Acetazolamide (Diamox)
    • Dichlorphenamide (Daranide)
    • Methazolamide (Neptazane)
  — Topical
    • Brinzolamide (Azopt)
    • Dorzolamide (Trusopt)
- *Combination therapy*
  — Timolol maleate and dorzolamide (Cosopt)
- *Hyperosmolar agents*
  — Glycerin liquid (Ophthalgan, Osmoglyn Oral)
  — Isosorbide solution (Ismotic)
  — Mannitol solution (Osmitrol)

Cataracts

- Clouding or opacity of the lens
- Early signs
  — Blurred vision
  — Decreased color perception
- Late signs
  — Double vision
  — Clouded pupil

Nursing and Collaborative Management for Cataract Removal

- Preoperative
  — Assess medications being taken
  — Stop anticoagulants before surgery
  — Teach client how to instill eye drops
- Postoperative
  — Wear eye shield while sleeping
  — Avoid lifting > 10 lb
  — Avoid lying on operative side and valsalva maneuver
  — Report signs of increased intraocular pressure
    • Acute pain
    • Loss of peripheral vision
    • Visual field defects

Eye Trauma/Injury

- Trauma
  — Determine type of injury
  — Position client in sitting position to reduce intraocular pressure
  — Never attempt to remove embedded object
  — Irrigate eye if a chemical injury has occurred
- Detached retina
  — Described as a curtain falling over the visual field
  — Painless
  — Client may see black spots or floaters (indicates bleeding has occurred with detachment)
  — Retina is repaired surgically
  — Keep eye patch over affected area

Hearing Loss

- Conductive hearing loss
  — Sounds do not travel to the inner ear
  — Client may benefit from hearing aid.
- Sensorineural hearing loss
  — Sound distorted by defect in inner ear
- Common causes
  — Infection
  — Ototoxic drugs
    • Gentamicin
    • Vancomycin
    • Lasix
  — Trauma
  — Aging
- Assessment
  — Inability to hear whisper from 1 to 2 feet
  — Shouting in conversations
  — Turning head to favor one ear
  — Loud volume on TV

9 Pediatric Nursing

The PN directs the unlicensed assistive personnel (UAP) to play with a 4-year-old child on bed rest. Which activity or activities should the PN recommend? (Select all that apply.)

A. Monopoly board game
B. Looking at picture books
C. Fifty-piece puzzle
D. Hand puppets
E. Coloring book

HESI Test Question Approach			
Positive?		YES	NO
Key Words			
Rephrase			
Rule Out Choices			
A	B	C	D

Growth and Development

Know the norms for growth and development!

- Infant
  — Doubles birth weight by 6 months, triples by 12 months
  — Plays "peek-a-boo" by 6 months
  — Sits upright without support by 8 months
  — Develops fine pincer grasp by 10 to 12 months (can pick up Cheerios)
- Toddler (1 to 3 years)
  — Throws ball overhand at 18 months
  — Produces two- to three-word sentences at 2 years
  — Begins toilet training around 2 years
  — Ritualistic
  — No concept of time
  — Frequent tantrums
- Preschool-Age Child (3 to 5 years)
  — Rides tricycle at 3 years
  — Favorite word is WHY
  — Can construct sentences of five to eight words
- School-Age Child (6-12 years)
  — Each year gains 4 to 6 lb, grows 2 inches
  — Learns to tell time
  — Socialization with peers important
- Adolescent (12-19 years)
  — Rapid growth—second only to first year of life!
  — Develops secondary sex characteristics

One hour after receiving IV antibiotics for sepsis, a 2-month-old infant is crying inconsolably, despite the mother's presence. The nurse recognizes that the infant is exhibiting symptoms related to which likely condition?

A. Allergic reaction to the antibiotics
B. Pain related to IV infiltration
C. Separation anxiety from mother
D. Hunger and thirst

HESI Test Question Approach			
Positive?		YES	NO
Key Words			
Rephrase			
Rule Out Choices			
A	B	C	D

Pain Assessment and Management
- Assessment is based on verbal and nonverbal cues from child and includes parents' information.
- Use appropriate pain scales.
- Safety is a major priority for administering medication.
- Make sure dose is SAFE for child's age and weight.

Immunization Teaching
- Common cold is NOT a contraindication to immunization unless fever > 99° F.
- Normal after injection: Fever < 102° F, redness and soreness at site for 2 to 3 days.
- Call physician if high-pitched crying, seizures, or high fever occur.
- Use acetaminophen orally.
- Consult immunization chart: *www.cdc.gov/vaccines/recs/schedules/childhood immunizations*.
- NOTE: Withhold MMR vaccine if client has a history of an anaphylactic reaction to neomycin or eggs.

Example: Which vaccines would the nurse expect to be prescribed for a 2-month-old brought into the pediatrician's office for a well baby checkup?

Answer: DTaP, HepB, HIB, IPV, and PCV

Communicable Diseases
The incidence of common childhood communicable diseases has declined greatly since the advent of immunizations, but they do occur, and nurses should be able to identify the infection, including:
— Measles
— Rubeola
— Rubella
— Roseola
— Mumps
— Pertussis
— Chickenpox
— Diphtheria
— Erythema infectiosum (fifth disease)
- Treat fever caused by infection with acetaminophen, not ASA (acetylsalicylic acid, aspirin).

- Isolation is required during the infectious phase.
- Teaching is the primary intervention for preventing the spread of disease.
- Provide supportive measures until disease runs its course.

Poisonings

- Frequent cause of childhood injury—teach poison-proofing methods for the home!
- GI disturbance is a common symptom.
- Caustic poisonings cause burns of the mouth and pharynx.
- Identify poisonous agent quickly!
- Assess ABCs.
- Teach parents NOT to make the child vomit, which may cause more damage.
- Call Poison Control Center or 911, depending on how the child is acting.

The nurse is performing the initial assessment of a 2-year-old child suspected of having bacterial epiglottitis. Which of the following is necessary?
A. Use a tongue depressor to assess for erythema
B. Obtain a throat swab for culture and sensitivity
C. Observe for the presence of drooling
D. Measure pain using a FACES scale

HESI Test Question Approach			
Positive?		YES	NO
Key Words			
Rephrase			
Rule Out Choices			
A	B	C	D

Respiratory Disorders

A 4-year-old is brought to the clinic with a fever of 103° F, a sore throat, and moderate respiratory distress caused by a suspected bacterial infection. Which medical diagnosis is a contraindication to obtaining a throat culture in the child?
A. Tonsillitis
B. Streptococcal infection
C. Bronchiolitis
D. Epiglottitis

HESI Test Question Approach			
Positive?		YES	NO
Key Words			
Rephrase			
Rule Out Choices			
A	B	C	D

Common Respiratory Disorders

- Be familiar with normal values for respiratory and pulse rates for children.
- Know cardinal and other signs of respiratory distress.
- Respiratory failure usually occurs before cardiac failure.

Pulmonary Infections

- Nasopharyngitis
- Tonsillitis
  - May be viral or bacterial
  - Check prothrombin time (PT) and partial thromboplastin time (PTT) before surgery
  - Monitor for bleeding
  - Highest risk for bleeding is during first 24 hours and 5 to 10 days postoperative
- Otitis media
  - S/S—fever, pulling at ear
  - Discharge from ear
  - Administer antibiotics
  - Reduce temperature to prevent seizures
- Bacterial tracheitis
- Bronchitis
- Respiratory syncytial virus (RSV) bronchiolitis
  - Isolate the child (contact isolation)
  - Monitor respiratory status
  - Administer antiviral agent (ribavirin aerosols)
  - Maintain patent airway
- Epiglottitis
  - S/S—high fever, sore throat, muffled voice, tripod position
  - IV antibiotics
  - Do not examine throat; may cause complete airway obstruction
  - Be prepared for tracheostomy

Asthma

- Leading cause of chronic illness in children
- Allergies influence persistence and severity

Nursing and Collaborative Management

- S/S—tight cough, expiratory wheezing, peak flow levels
- Monitor for respiratory distress, need for O_2 nebulizer therapy
- Reinforce education on use of peak flow meter, nebulization treatments, and multidose inhalers
- Refer to section on drug therapy for asthma and COPD in Chapter 5

The PN is reinforcing teaching for a school-age child and the child's parent about the administration of inhaled betamethasone dipropionate (QVAR, a corticosteroid) and albuterol (Proventil, a bronchodilator) for the treatment of asthma. Which statement by the parent indicates that teaching has been effective?

A. "I'll keep the inhalers in the refrigerator."
B. "We only need to use the inhalers when the peak flow numbers are in the red."
C. "We will take the bronchodilator first, then the corticosteroid."
D. "I will take the corticosteroid first, wait a few minutes, and then take the bronchodilator."

HESI Test Question Approach			
Positive?		YES	NO
Key Words			
Rephrase			
Rule Out Choices			
A	B	C	D

Cystic Fibrosis (CF)

- Most common inherited disease of Caucasian children
- Diagnosis may be based on a number of criteria
  - Identification of CF mutations
  - Absence of pancreatic enzymes
  - Steatorrhea
  - Chronic pulmonary involvement
  - Positive newborn screening test
  - First sign may be meconium ileus at birth
  - High sweat chloride concentration (pilocarpine test or sweat test)
  - Delayed growth; poor weight gain

Nursing Management

- Pancreatic enzymes with each meal and snacks
- Fat-soluble vitamins
- Teach family percussion and postural drainage techniques

Cardiovascular Disorders

Congenital Heart Disorders

- Acyanotic types: All have L-to-R shunt
  - Ventricular septal defect
  - Atrial septal defect
  - Patent ductus arteriosus
  - Coarctation of the aorta
  - Aortic stenosis
- Cyanotic types:
  - Tetralogy of Fallot
  - Truncus arteriosus
  - Transposition of the great vessels

Congestive Heart Failure

- Common complication of congenital heart disorders
- Early S/S—longer period for feeding; may fail to gain weight; may be irritable and fatigued
- Later S/S—pedal edema, neck vein distention, cyanosis, tachycardia, tachypnea, coughing, retractions, wheezing, grunting

Nursing and Collaborative Management

- Monitor vital signs, elevate head of bed, administer O_2
- Weigh daily on same scale
- Digoxin, diuretics, and ACE inhibitors

Digoxin Precautions

- Count apical rate when child is at rest; withhold medication if pulse is:
  - <90 to 110 beats/min a general rule, the drug is not given if the pulse is below 90 to 110 beats/min in infants and young children or below 70 beats/min in older children (the cutoff point for adults is 60 beats/min). However, because the pulse rate varies in children in different age groups, the written drug order should specify at what heart rate the drug is withheld
  - <70 beats in older children
  - Notify healthcare provider if pulse is below these rates

- Do not skip or try to make up doses
- Give 1 to 2 hours before meals
- Watch for S/S of toxicity and teach them to parents:
  — Vomiting, anorexia, diarrhea, muscle weakness, drowsiness
- Provide adequate potassium in the diet

Rheumatic Fever
- Peaks in school-age children
- Most common cause of acquired heart disease
- Affects connective tissue
- S/S—sore throat, which appears to be improving; then, fever develops, along with rash, chorea, and an elevated erythrocyte sedimentation rate

Nursing and Collaborative Management
- Encourage compliance with drug regimens
  — Penicillin remains the drug of choice
  — Salicylates are used to control the inflammatory process and to reduce fever and discomfort
  — Prednisone may be indicated in some clients with heart failure
- Facilitate recovery from the illness
  — Stress bed rest or at least limited activity during the acute illness
  — Support secondary prophylaxis
  — Provide emotional support

The PN reviews the medication record of a 2-month-old and notes that the infant was given a scheduled dose of digoxin with a documented apical pulse of 76 beats/min. What action should the nurse take first?
A. Assess the current apical heart rate
B. Observe for the onset of diarrhea
C. Complete an adverse occurrence report
D. Determine the serum potassium level

HESI Test Question Approach			
Positive?		YES	NO
Key Words			
Rephrase			
Rule Out Choices			
A	B	C	D

Neurological and Muscular Disorders

The PN is caring for a 16-year-old with Down syndrome in a group home. The teenager has a mental age of 5. Which priority nursing action should be included in the plan of care?
A. Monitoring for hearing loss
B. Monitoring intake and output (I & O)
C. Providing a dependable routine
D. Providing a quiet environment

HESI Test Question Approach			
Positive?		YES	NO
Key Words			
Rephrase			
Rule Out Choices			
A	B	C	D

Down Syndrome

- Flat, broad nasal bridge; upward, outward slant of eyes
- Commonly associated problems
  - Cardiac defects
  - Delayed development
  - Respiratory problems
- Always evaluate mental age
- Feed to back and side of mouth because of tongue thrust
- Refer family to early intervention program

NCLEX-PN Exam questions are likely to focus on supporting the child and the parent(s) in order to enable the child to achieve the highest level of functioning.

Cerebral Palsy (CP)

- Diagnosis is made through evaluation of the child; findings include:
  - Persistent neonatal reflexes after 6 months
  - Spasticity
  - Scissoring of the legs
  - Tight abductor muscles of the hips
  - Tightening of the heel cord
  - Absence of parachute reflex

Nursing and Collaborative Management

- Prevent aspiration with feedings
- Administer phenytoin (Dilantin) for seizures
- Administer diazepam (Valium) for muscle spasms

Spina Bifida Occulta

- No sac present
- Suspect if tuft of hair is present at base of spine

Menigocele

- Contains only meninges and spinal fluid
- No nerves present in spinal sac

Myelomenigocele

- Sac contains spinal fluid, meninges, and nerves
- Child has sensory and motor defects
- Preoperative/postoperative care
  - Monitor urine output
  - Watch for $\uparrow$ ICP
  - Keep sac free of stool and urine
  - Measure head circumference every 8 hours and check fontanels
  - Be alert for signs of latex allergy

A child with hydrocephalus is 1 day postoperative for revision of a ventriculoatrial shunt. Which finding is most important?

A. Increased blood pressure
B. Increased temperature
C. Increased serum glucose
D. Increased hematocrit

HESI Test Question Approach		
Positive?	**YES**	**NO**
Key Words		
Rephrase		
Rule Out Choices		
A	B	C	D

Hydrocephalus

- Abnormal accumulation of cerebrospinal fluid (CSF)
- Symptoms
  - ↑ Intracranial pressure (ICP)
  - ↑ BP
  - ↓ Pulse
  - Changes in level of consciousness
  - Irritability, vomiting

Nursing and Collaborative Management

- Elevate head of bed
- Use seizure precautions
- Prepare for shunt placement
- Assess for shunt malfunctioning
- Monitor for S/S of infection
- Teach parent(s) about shunt replacement

Seizures or Epilepsy

- More common in children < 2 years
- Seizures types
  - Generalized tonic/clonic
  - Grand mal seizure with loss of consciousness
    - Aura precedes seizure.
    - Tonic phase—stiffness of body
    - Clonic phase—spasms and relaxation
    - Postictal phase—sleepy and disoriented
  - Petit mal
    - Momentary loss of consciousness
    - Child appears to be daydreaming
    - Lasts 5 to 10 seconds

Nursing and Collaborative Management

- Maintain patent airway
- Keep side rails up
- Pad side rails
- Administer anticonvulsants
- Document interventions
- Reinforce teaching to family and client about medications

Anticonvulsants

- Phenobarbital
- Primidone (Mysoline)
- Phenytoin (Dilantin)
- Valproic acid (Depakene)
- Clonazepam (Rivotril)
- Carbamazepine (Tegretol)

Bacterial Meningitis

- Signs and symptoms
  — Older children: S/S of increased ICP, neck stiffness, + Kernig's sign, + Brudzinski's sign
  — Infants: Classic signs absent; poor feeding, vomiting, irritability, bulging fontanels
- Diagnostic procedures include lumbar puncture to obtain sample for laboratory analysis

Nursing and Collaborative Management

- Isolate client for at least 24 hours
- Administer antibiotics
- Obtain VS and perform neurological checks frequently
- Assess for ↑ ICP, muscle twitching, and changes in LOC
- Measure head circumference daily
- Syndrome of inappropriate antidiuretic hormone (SIADH) occurs frequently
- Fluid restrictions may be necessary

Reye's Syndrome

- Etiology is often but NOT ALWAYS associated with aspirin use and influenza or varicella infection
- Rapidly progressing encephalopathy
- S/S—lethargy progressing to coma, vomiting, hypo-glycemia

Nursing and Collaborative Management

- Maintain airway
- Neurological checks
- Administer Mannitol for ICP control
- Early diagnosis is important to improve client outcome

Muscular Dystrophy (MD)
Duchenne MD

- Onset between 2 and 6 years of age
- Most severe and most common MD of childhood

Diagnosis

- Muscle biopsy shows degeneration of muscle fibers and replacement with connective tissue and fat
- Serum creatine phosphokinase (CK) levels are extremely high in the first 2 years of life, before onset of the disease

Symptoms

- Delayed walking
- Frequent falls
- Tiring easily when walking

Nursing and Collaborative Management
- Exercise
- Preventing falls
- Assistive devices for ambulation

Renal Disorders in Children

Urinary Tract Infection (UTI)
- More common in girls
- Symptoms
  - Poor food intake
  - Strong-smelling urine
  - Fever
  - Pain with urination

Nursing and Collaborative Management
- Obtain urine culture before starting antibiotics
- Teach home care
  - Finish all antibiotics
  - Avoid bubble baths
  - Increase intake of acidic fluids (e.g., apple or cranberry juice)

Vesicoureteral Reflux
- Retrograde flow of urine into the ureters
- Symptoms
  - Recurrent UTIs
  - Common with neurogenic bladder

Nursing and Collaborative Management
- Teach child/parent(s) measures to prevent UTIs
- Record output after catheterization
- Maintain hydration

Acute Glomerulonephritis (AGN)
- Common features
  - Oliguria, hematuria, proteinuria
  - Edema
  - Hypertension
  - Circulatory congestion

Assessment
- Recent strep infection
- Dark ("iced tea") urine
- Irritable and/or lethargic

Nursing and Collaborative Management
- Maintenance of fluid balance
- Treatment of hypertension
- Common nursing interventions
  - Vital signs every 4 hours
  - Daily weights
  - Low-sodium, low-potassium diet

Nephrotic Syndrome
Nephrotic syndrome is characterized by increased glomerular permeability to protein.

102

Assessment
- Frothy urine
- Massive proteinuria
- Edema
- Anorexia

Nursing and Collaborative Management
- Reduce excretion of protein
- Reduce or prevent fluid retention
- Prevent infections
- Common interventions
  - Skin care
  - Administer medications
  - Diuretics
  - Corticosteroid therapy
  - Immunosuppressants
  - Small, frequent feedings
  - Discharge teaching
  - Daily weights
  - Side effects of medications

Acute Renal Failure Management
- Treatment of the underlying cause
- Management of complications of renal failure
- Providing supportive therapy

Chronic Kidney Disease
- Characterized by:
  - Waste product retention
  - Water and sodium retention
  - Hyperkalemia
  - Acidosis
  - Calcium and phosphorus disturbance
  - Anemia
  - Hypertension
  - Growth disturbances

Home Dialysis
Nursing and Collaborative Management
- Educate family about:
  - Disease, its implications, and the therapeutic plan
  - Possible psychological effects
  - Treatment and technical aspects of the procedure
  - Major concerns in kidney transplantation
    - Tissue matching
    - Preventing rejection
    - Psychological concerns
    - Self-image issues related to body changes arising from corticosteroid therapy

A school-age child with nephrotic syndrome is seen at the clinic 2 days after discharge from the hospital. Which assessment is most important after discharge?
A. Pain
B. Capillary refill
C. Urine ketones
D. Daily weight

<table>
<tr><td colspan="4">HESI Test Question Approach</td></tr>
<tr><td>Positive?</td><td></td><td>YES</td><td>NO</td></tr>
<tr><td>Key Words</td><td></td><td></td><td></td></tr>
<tr><td></td><td></td><td></td><td></td></tr>
<tr><td></td><td></td><td></td><td></td></tr>
<tr><td>Rephrase</td><td></td><td></td><td></td></tr>
<tr><td></td><td></td><td></td><td></td></tr>
<tr><td></td><td></td><td></td><td></td></tr>
<tr><td>Rule Out Choices</td><td></td><td></td><td></td></tr>
<tr><td>A</td><td>B</td><td>C</td><td>D</td></tr>
</table>

Gastrointestinal Disorders

Nutritional Assessment
- Present nutritional status
- Body mass index
- Dietary history
- Past nutrition assessment
- Height
- Weight
- Head circumference
- Skinfold thickness
- Arm circumference
- Iron deficiency
  — For $FeSO_4$ drops: Use straw; give with orange juice, not with dairy foods

Diarrhea
- Worldwide, the leading cause of death in children younger than age 5 years
- Classified as acute or chronic
- Common problem for infants

Symptoms
- Depressed, sunken eyes
- Weight loss
- Decreased urine output

Nursing and Collaborative Management
- Fluid and electrolyte balance
- Rehydration
- Maintenance fluid therapy
- Reintroduction of adequate diet
- Do not give antidiarrheal agents

Cleft Lip or Cleft Palate
- Malformation of the face or oral cavity
- Initial closure of cleft lip is performed if infant's health is good at or around 10-12 weeks of age
- Closure of cleft palate is performed at about 7-15 months

Nursing and Collaborative Management
- Promote bonding
- Use Breck or Habermann feeder

- Maintain airway
- Do not use straws or spoons
- Feed only soft foods if child has cleft palate
- Post operatively prevent the child from excessive crying, which could cause tension on the suture line, and carefully position (never on the abdomen)

Pyloric Stenosis
- Common in first-born males
- Vomiting becomes projectile around day 14 after birth

Intussusception
- Telescoping of part of the intestine
- Requires emergency intervention
- Provide perioperative care for client undergoing repair

Congenital Aganglionic Megacolon (Hirschsprung's Disease)
- Requires series of surgeries to correct
- Temporary colostomy is needed

Hematologic Disorders

Iron Deficiency Anemia
- Common in infants, toddlers, and adolescent females
- Review Hgb norms for children
- Teach family about administering oral iron

Sickle Cell Anemia
- Autosomal recessive disorder
- Fetal Hgb does not sickle
- Hydration to promote hemodilution

Nursing and Collaborative Management
- Crisis marked by fever and pain
- Promote adequate oxygenation
- Keep well hydrated
- Do not give supplemental iron
- Give folic acid orally

Hemophilia
- X-linked recessive disorder

Nursing and Collaborative Management
- Administer fresh frozen plasma
- Increased risk of bleeding
  — Apply pressure to sites of even minor bleeding

Metabolic and Endocrine Disorders

Phenylketonuria (PKU)
- Autosomal recessive disorder
- Newborn screening with Guthrie test
  — Done at birth and at 3 weeks
- Strict adherence to low-phenylalanine diet
- Special PKU formula
- Avoid meat, milk, dairy, and eggs
- Eat fruits, juices, cereal, bread, and starches

Diabetes Mellitus

Obesity

- Of children age 6 to 11, 19% are categorized as overweight or obese.
- Excess weight and obesity in childhood may lead to adult obesity, with increased risks of cardiovascular disease and type 2 diabetes.
- Minorities are disproportionally at risk.
- Parental obesity is the highest predictor of childhood obesity.
- BMI, dietary, and activity assessments should be obtained and evaluated.

Types of Diabetes Mellitus

- Type 1
  - An immune-mediated disease associated with absolute insulin deficiency. The body's own T cells destroy pancreatic beta cells, the source of insulin. Type 1 diabetes is common is school-age children.
- Type 2
  - A disease in which the defect is insulin resistance and/or relative insulin deficiency. It is marked by insufficient insulin production, insulin resistance, and/or excessive and unregulated glucose production by the liver.

Classic Symptoms of Diabetes

- Polyuria, polyphagia, polydipsia, and weight loss; child may wet the bed

Nursing and Collaborative Management

- Consider child's cognitive level and age when planning/teaching:
  - Dietary changes
  - Need for exercise
  - Insulin administration
  - Avoid hypoglycemia
- Continuous follow up is important

Skeletal Disorders

Assessment

- Visible signs of fractures
- Obtain baseline pulses, color, movement, sensation, temperature, swelling, and pain
- Report any changes immediately

Traction

- Buck's traction
  - For knee immobilization
- Russell's traction
  - For fracture of femur or lower leg
- Dunlop's traction
  - Can be skeletal or skin
- 90°/90° traction

Nursing and Collaborative Management

- Monitor neurovascular status (5 Ps)
- Provide appropriate toys
- Teach cast care to family
  - Prevent soiling of cast with careful diapering

Congenital Dislocated Hip
Assessment
- Positive Ortolani's sign
- Unequal fold of skin on buttocks
- Limited abduction of hip
- Treated by surgical correction

Nursing and Collaborative Management
- Postoperative interventions
- Hip spica cast care
- Apply Pavlik harness (worn 24 hr/day)

Scoliosis
- S-shaped curvature of the spine
- Most common nontraumatic skeletal condition in children
- Affects both genders at any age, but most commonly seen in adolescents

Juvenile Rheumatoid Arthritis (JRA)
- Most common arthritic condition of childhood
- Inflammatory diseases involving the joints, connective tissues, and viscera
- Exact cause unknown, but infections and autoimmune response have been implicated
- Therapy consists of administration of medications, (e.g., NSAIDs, methotrexate, or aspirin); exercise; heat application; and support of joints

The PN walks into a hospital room and observes a teenage client experiencing a tonic-clonic seizure. Which intervention should the nurse provide first?
A. Restrain the client to protect against injury
B. Flex the neck to ensure stabilization
C. Use a tongue blade to open the airway
D. Turn the client on the side to aid ventilation

The healthcare provider prescribes the anticonvulsant phenytoin (Dilantin) for an adolescent with a seizure disorder. The nurse should instruct the client to notify the healthcare provider if which condition develops?
A. Dry mouth
B. Dizziness
C. Sore throat
D. Gingival hyperplasia

HESI Test Question Approach				
Positive?			**YES**	**NO**
Key Words				
Rephrase				
Rule Out Choices				
A	B		C	D

HESI Test Question Approach				
Positive?			**YES**	**NO**
Key Words				
Rephrase				
Rule Out Choices				
A	B		C	D

10 Maternal-Newborn Health Nursing

A client who has reached 36 weeks' gestation is placed in the lithotomy position. She suddenly complains of feeling breathless and lightheaded, and she shows marked pallor. What action should the nurse take first?
A. Turn the client to a lateral position
B. Place the client in Trendelenburg's position
C. Obtain vital signs and a pulse oximetry reading
D. Initiate distraction techniques

HESI Test Question Approach		
Positive?	YES	NO
Key Words		
Rephrase		
Rule Out Choices		
A	B	C	D

Pregnancy: Key Assessments

- Assess for violence.
  - Battering, emotional or physical abuse can begin with pregnancy.
  - Assess for abuse in private, away from male partner.
  - The nurse needs to know:
    - Local resources
    - How to determine client's safety
- Gravidity and parity
  - Gravida—number of times a female has been pregnant, regardless of outcome
  - Para—number of deliveries (not children) that occurred after 20 weeks' gestation
    - Multiple births count as one
    - Loss of pregnancy before 20 weeks counted as abortion, but add 1 to gravidity
    - Fetal demise after 20 weeks added to parity
- GTPAL
  G Gravidity: pregnancy
  T Term pregnancies
  P Preterm pregnancies
  A Abortions (elective or spontaneous)
  L Living children
- Gestation
  - Naegele's rule
    - Count back 3 months from date of last normal menstrual period
    - Add 1 year and 7 days
    - *Example:* If the last menstrual period was May 2, 2014, the EDB would be February 9, 2015.
- Fundal height
  - 12 to 13 weeks: Fundus rises out of symphysis
  - 20 weeks: Fundus is at the umbilicus
  - 24 to about 36 weeks: Fundal height (in cm) from the symphysis is equal to the number of weeks of gestation if this is a single pregnancy

- Maternal psychological changes
  - Ambivalence occurs early in pregnancy, even with a planned pregnancy.
  - Acceptance occurs with the woman's readiness for the experience and her identification with the motherhood role.
  - *Emotional lability* refers to the frequent changes in emotional states or extremes of emotional states sometimes seen in pregnancy.

A client's suspected pregnancy is confirmed. The client tells the PN that she has had previous pregnancies: she delivered a single child at 39 weeks; twins at 34 weeks; and a single child at 35 weeks. Using the GTPAL notation system, how should the PN record the client's gravidity and parity?

A. 3-0-3-0-3
B. 3-1-1-1-3
C. 4-1-2-0-4
D. 4-2-1-0-3

HESI Test Question Approach			
Positive?		YES	NO
Key Words			
Rephrase			
Rule Out Choices			
A	B	C	D

A client who is 72 hours post cesarean section is preparing to go home. She complains to the PN that she can't get the baby's diaper on "right." Which action should the nurse take?

A. Demonstrate how to diaper the baby correctly
B. Observe the client diapering the baby while offering praise and hints
C. Call the social worker for long-term follow-up
D. Reassure the client that she knows how to take care of her baby

HESI Test Question Approach			
Positive?		YES	NO
Key Words			
Rephrase			
Rule Out Choices			
A	B	C	D

Complications of Childbearing

Chronic Hypertension

- Hypertension and/or proteinuria in pregnant woman; chronic hypertension—before 20 weeks of gestation; persistent hypertension—12 weeks postpartum

Superimposed Preeclampsia or Eclampsia

- Development of preeclampsia or eclampsia in a woman with chronic hypertension before 20 weeks of gestation

Preeclampsia/Eclampsia
Preeclampsia Symptoms
- BP
  - *Mild:* 30 mmHg systolic and/or 15 mmHg diastolic over baseline
  - *Severe:* Same (some sources say 160/110 mmHg × 2 or more)
- Protein
  - Mild: >1+
  - Severe: 3+ to 4+
- Edema
  - *Mild:* Eyes, face, fingers
  - *Severe:* Generalized edema
- Deep tendon reflexes (DTRs)
  - *Mild:* May be normal
  - *Severe:* 3+ or more and clonus
- Central nervous system (CNS) symptoms
  - *Mild:* Headache, irritability
  - *Severe:* Severe headache, visual disturbances
- Other
  - Weight gain > 2 lb/week
  - Oliguria (<100 mL/4 hr); epigastric pain related to liver enlargement
  - Elevated serum creatinine, thrombocytopenia; marked SGOT elevation

Common Nursing Interventions—Preeclampsia
- Control stimulation in room
- Explain procedures
- Maintain IV (16- to 18-g venocatheter)
- Monitor BP every 15 to 30 minutes
- Monitor urine for protein every 1 hour
- The healthcare provider may prescribe magnesium sulfate

Nursing Interventions—Eclampsia (Seizures)
- Stay with client
- Turn client to side
- Do not attempt to force objects into client's mouth
- Administer O_2 and have suction available

Gestational Diabetes
Screening
- Recommendations for glucose screening for all pregnant women
  - 1-hour glucose screening between 24 and 26 weeks
  - Goal is strict blood glucose control
  - Generally, Glyburide or insulin is used during pregnancy. Insulin does not cross the placenta, and Glyburide minimally crosses it.

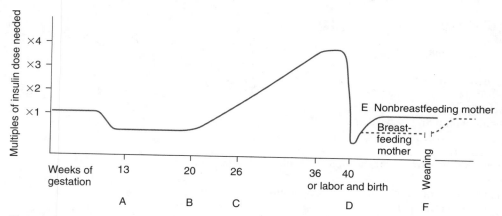

Figure 10-1 Changing insulin needs during pregnancy. (From Lowdermilk D, Perry S, Cashion K, Alden KR: *Maternity and women's health care*, ed 10, St. Louis, 2012, Mosby.)

A client who has gestational diabetes asks the PN to explain why her baby is at risk for macrosomia. Which explanation should the nurse offer?

A. The placenta receives decreased maternal blood flow during pregnancy because of vascular constriction.

B. The fetus secretes insulin in response to maternal hyperglycemia, causing weight gain and growth.

C. Infants of diabetic mothers are postmature, which allows the fetus extra time to grow.

D. Rapid fetal growth contributes to congenital anomalies, which are more common in infants of diabetic mothers.

Preterm Labor (PTL)

Signs and Symptoms

- More than five contractions in an hour; menstrual-like cramps
- Low, dull backache
- Pelvic pressure
- Increase/change in vaginal discharge
- Leaking or gush of amniotic fluid

Tocolytics and Their Administration

A number of medications can be used to stop uterine contractions.

- Ritodrine (Yutopar)
  — Side effects
    - Nervousness, tremulousness
    - Headache
    - N/V, diarrhea, epigastric pain
  — Adverse effects
    - Tachycardia
    - Chest pain with pulmonary edema
    - Low K^+, hyperglycemia
  — Nursing interventions
    - Maternal ECG and lab tests
    - Cardiac and fetal monitoring
    - VS every 15 min
  — Antidote
    - Propranolol (Inderal)

HESI Test Question Approach			
Positive?		**YES**	**NO**
Key Words			
Rephrase			
Rule Out Choices			
A	**B**	**C**	**D**

- Terbutaline (Brethine)
  — Side effects
    - Nervousness, tremulousness
    - Headache
    - N/V, diarrhea, epigastric pain
  — Adverse effects
    - Tachycardia
    - Chest pain with pulmonary edema
    - Low K^+, hyperglycemia
  — Nursing interventions
    - Notify healthcare provider if the woman exhibits the following:
      □ Maternal heart rate greater than 130 beats/min; arrhythmias, chest pain
      □ BP less than 90/60 mm Hg
      □ Signs of pulmonary edema (e.g., dyspnea, crackles, decreased SaO_2)
      □ Fetal heart rate greater than 180 beats/min
    - Hyperglycemia occurs more frequently in women who are being treated simultaneously with corticosteroids
    - Ensure that the antidote, propranolol (Inderal), is available to reverse adverse effects related to cardiovascular function
    - Monitor I & O
    - Check weight daily
- Magnesium sulfate
  — Side effects
    - CNS depression
    - Slowed respirations
    - Decreased DTRs
  — Adverse effects
    - Decreased urine output
    - Pulmonary edema
  — Nursing interventions
    - Hold if
      □ Respirations < 12 breaths/min
      □ Urine output < 100 mL/4 hr
      □ Absent DTRs
    - Monitor serum magnesium levels - with higher doses; therapeutic range is between 4 and 7.5 mEq/L or 5-8 mg/dl
  — Antidote
    - Ensure that calcium gluconate 1 g (10 ml of 10% solution) is available for emergency administration to reverse magnesium sulfate toxicity
- Other drugs used to reduce contractions
    - Indomethacin (Indocin)
    - Nifedipine (Procardia)

A client at 15 weeks' gestation is admitted for an inevitable abortion. Thirty minutes after her return from surgery, her vital signs are stable. Which nursing intervention has the highest priority?

A. Ask the client whether she would like to talk about losing her baby.
B. Place cold cabbage leaves on the client's breasts to reduce breast engorgement.
C. Send a referral to the grief counselor for at-home follow-up.
D. Confirm the client's Rh and Coombs status and administer RhoGAM if indicated.

HESI Test Question Approach			
Positive?		YES	NO
Key Words			
Rephrase			
Rule Out Choices			
A	B	C	D

Miscarriage

Assessment

- Vaginal bleeding at week 20 of gestation or earlier
- Uterine cramping, backache, pelvic pressure
- May have symptoms of shock
- Assess client's and family members' emotional status, needs, and support

Nursing Interventions

- Monitor VS, LOC, and amount of bleeding
- Prepare client to receive IV fluids and/or blood
- If client is Rh negative, give RhoGAM

Incompetent Cervix

- Recurrent premature dilation of the cervix; defined as passive and painless dilation of the cervix during the second trimester
- Conservative management
  — Bed rest
  — Hydration
  — Tocolysis (inhibition of uterine contractions)
- Cervical cerclage may be performed.
  — McDonald cerclage—a band of homologous fascia or nonabsorbable ribbon (Mersilene) may be placed around the cervix beneath the mucosa to constrict the internal os of the cervix.
  — Cerclage procedure can be classified according to time or whether it is elective (prophylactic), urgent, or emergent.

Ectopic Pregnancy

Assessment

- Missed period, but early signs of pregnancy absent
- Positive result on pregnancy test
- Rupture
  — Sharp, unilateral pelvic pain
  — Vaginal bleeding
  — Referred shoulder pain
  — Syncope (can lead to shock)

Nursing Interventions
- Monitor client's hemodynamic status
- Prepare client for surgery and administration of IV fluids, including blood

Abruptio Placentae and Placenta Previa
Abruptio Placentae
- Concealed or overt bleeding
- Uterine tone ranges from tense without relaxation to tense and boardlike
- Persistently painful
  - Abnormal fetal heart rate - Nonreassuring fetal heart rate pattern

Placenta Previa
- Bright red vaginal bleeding
- Soft uterine tone
- Painless
- FHR is normal unless bleeding is severe and mother becomes hypovolemic

Disseminated Intravascular Coagulation (DIC)
- Risk factors for DIC in pregnancy
  - Fetal demise
  - Infection/sepsis
  - Pregnancy-induced hypertension (preeclampsia)
  - Abruptio placentae

Dystocia
Dystocia is a difficult birth, which occurs as a result of problems involving one or more of the 5 *P*s (powers, passage, passenger, psyche, position); for example, lack of progress in cervical dilation; delay in fetal descent; or a change in the characteristics of uterine contraction.

Labor and Delivery
- Stages of Labor
  - First Stage - Stage of dilation and effacement and complete with 100% cervical effacement and complete dilation of cervix (10 cm). Duration is from 8 to 20 hours in the primipara and 5 to 14 hours in the multipara.
  - Second Stage –Stage of expulsion and ends with birth of the baby. Generally lasts from a few minutes to 2 hours.
  - Third Stage is labeled the placental separation stage. It begins with the birth of the baby and ends with the expulsion of the placenta. This process can last up to 30 minutes, with an average length of 5 to 10 minutes.

External fetal monitoring is noninvasive and is performed with a Toco transducer or Doppler ultrasonic transducer.

Internal fetal monitoring is invasive; the membranes must be ruptured, and an electrode must be attached to the presenting part of the fetus.

Types of Regional Blocks Used to Manage Labor Discomfort

- Pudendal block
  - Given in second stage
  - Has no effect on pain of uterine contractions
- Peridural (epidural or caudal) block
  - Given in first or second stage
  - Single dose or given continuously
  - May prolong second stage
- Intradural (subarachnoid, spinal)
  - Given in second stage
  - Rapid onset
  - Client must remain flat for 6 to 8 hours after delivery.

Postpartum Care

Fundal Involution

- Immediately the fundus is several centimeters below the umbilicus.
- Within 12 hours it rises to the umbilicus.
- The fundus descends 1 cm (a fingerbreadth) a day for 9 to 10 days, putting it below the symphysis pubis.
- It should be in the midline and firm.

Teaching Points

- Change pads as needed and with voiding and defecation. Wipe front to back.
- Good hand-washing technique
- Ice packs, sitz baths, peri bottle lavage, and topical anesthetic spray and pads
- Breast-feeding instructions
- Balances diet and fluid intake
- Rest/nap when baby sleeps
- Contraceptive use

Rh$_o$(D) Immune Globulin (RhoGAM)

- Given to Rh-negative women with possible exposure to Rh-positive blood
- Should have negative indirect Coombs test
- Given IM within 72 hours after delivery
- Must be checked by two nurses (blood product)

Rubella Vaccine

- Given subcutaneously to nonimmune client before discharge from hospital
- May breast-feed
- Do not give if client or family member is immunocompromised
- Avoid pregnancy for 2 to 3 months (teach contraception)

Postpartum Infections

- Perineal infections
- Endometritis
- Parametritis
- Peritonitis
- Mastitis
- Deep vein thrombosis
- Cystitis
- Pyelonephritis
- HIV, hepatitis, other STIs

Which nursing action has the highest priority for an infant immediately after birth?

A. Place the infant's head in the "sniff" position and give oxygen via face mask
B. Perform a bedside glucose test and feed the infant glucose water as needed
C. Assess the heart rate and perform chest compressions if the rate is below 60 beats/min
D. Dry the infant and place him or her under a radiant warmer or skin to skin with the mother

HESI Test Question Approach			
Positive?		**YES**	**NO**
Key Words			
Rephrase			
Rule Out Choices			
A	**B**	**C**	**D**

Newborn Parameters (Approximate)

- Length: 18 to 22 inches
- Weight: 5.5 to 9.5 lb
- Head circumference: 13.2 to 14 inches
- Sutures palpable with fontanels
- Fontanel closure
  — Anterior: By 18 months
  — Posterior: 6 to 8 weeks
- Umbilical cord should have three vessels: two arteries and one vein.
- Extremities should be flexed.
- Major gluteal folds should be even.
- Creases should be present on the soles of the feet.
- Ortolani's sign and Barlow's sign should be assessed for developmental dysplasia of the hip.
- Pulses should be palpable (radial, brachial, femoral).

Nursing Interventions

- Keep newborn warm.
- Suction airway as needed.
- Observe for respiratory distress.
- Normal or physiological jaundice appears after the first 24 hours in full-term newborns.
- Pathological jaundice occurs before this time and may indicate early hemolysis of red blood cells.
- Assess H & H and blood glucose levels.
- Weigh daily.
- Monitor intake and output; weigh diapers if necessary (1 g = 1 mL of urine).
- Monitor temperature.
- Observe for any cracks in the skin.
- Administer eye medication within 1 hour after birth.
- Provide cord care.
- Provide circumcision care. Teach client how to care for circumcision site.
- Position newborn on the right side after feeding; however, the side-lying position is not recommended for sleep, because this position makes it easy for the newborn to roll into the prone position.
- Observe for normal stool and the passage of meconium.
- Test newborn's reflexes.

Ages at Which Infant Reflexes Disappear

- Sucking or rooting: 3 to 4 months
- Moro: 3 to 4 months
- Tonic neck or fencing: 3 to 4 months
- Babinski's sign: 1 year to 18 months
- Palmar-plantar grasp: 8 months
- Stepping or walking: 3 to 4 months

Major Newborn Complications

Respiratory Distress Syndrome

- Causes inability to produce surfactant
- Results in hypoxia and acidosis

Meconium Aspiration Syndrome

- Fetal distress increases intestinal peristalsis
- Releases meconium into the amniotic fluid

Retinopathy of Prematurity

- Vascular disorder of the retina
- Caused by use of oxygen (>30 days)

Hyperbilirubinemia

- Elevated serum levels: >12 mg/dL
- Crucial to prevent kernicterus, which results in permanent neurological damage
- Jaundice starts at head, spreads to chest, abdomen, arms, legs, hands, and feet
- Treated with phototherapy—the use of fluorescent lights to reduce serum bilirubin levels
  - Possible adverse effects: Eye damage, dehydration, sensory deprivation
  - Expose as much of the skin as possible, but cover genital area
  - Cover eyes with eye shields
  - Monitor skin temperature closely
  - Increase fluids to compensate for water loss
  - Expect loose, green stools and green urine
  - Monitor newborn's skin color
  - Reposition every 2 hours
  - Provide stimulation
  - After treatment, continue monitoring for signs of rebound hyperbilirubinemia

Erythroblastosis Fetalis

- Destruction of red blood cells as a result of an antigen-antibody reaction
- Characterized by hemolytic anemia or hyperbilirubinemia
- Exchange of fetal and maternal blood occurs at birth. Antibodies are harmless to the mother but cause fetal hemolysis
- Administer $Rh_o(D)$ immune globulin
- Newborn's blood is replaced with Rh-negative blood to stop destruction of RBCs
- Rh-negative blood is gradually replaced with newborn's own blood

Sepsis

Presence of bacteria in the blood

TORCH Infections

TORCH group of infections includes:

T Toxoplasmosis

O Other infections (e.g., gonorrhea, syphilis, varicella, hepatitis B, HIV, or human parvovirus B19)

R Rubella

C Cytomegalovirus

H Herpes simplex virus

Addicted Newborn

- Passive addiction to drugs that have passed through the placenta

Fetal Alcohol Syndrome

- Caused by maternal alcohol use during pregnancy
- Causes mental and physical retardation

Newborn of a Mother with HIV

- Monitor antibody closely throughout pregnancy

Newborn of a Diabetic Mother

- Infant born to mother with insulin-dependent or gestational diabetes
- Hypoglycemia, hyperbilirubinemia, respiratory distress syndrome, hypocalcemia, birth trauma, and congenital anomalies may be present

A pregnant client tells the PN that she smokes only a few cigarettes a day. What information should the nurse provide the client about the effects of smoking during pregnancy?

A. Smoking causes vasoconstriction and reduces placental perfusion.

B. Smoking reduces the L:S ratio, contributing to lung immaturity.

C. Smoking causes vasodilation and fluid overload for the fetus.

D. Smoking places the fetus at risk for lung cancer.

HESI Test Question Approach		
Positive?	YES	NO
Key Words		
Rephrase		
Rule Out Choices		
A	B	C	D

Mental Health Nursing

An adult client is admitted to the in-client mental health unit for severe depression. Although the client has agreed to electroconvulsive therapy (ECT), the client's partner states, "I'm concerned that his neurons will be destroyed by this treatment." Which response by the practical nurse is most helpful?
A. "I'll contact the nurse supervisor for you."
B. "Let's tour the ECT room and speak to the staff."
C. "I think you should show support for your partner.
D. "May we sit and discuss your concerns about ECT?"

HESI Test Question Approach			
Positive?		YES	NO
Key Words			
Rephrase			
Rule Out Choices			
A	B	C	D

Therapeutic Communication
- Both verbal and nonverbal expression
- Goal directed
- Appropriate, effective, flexible; includes feedback

Important Definitions
Mental health: Successful adjustment to changing internal and external environments. Achieving mental health (and sustaining it) is a lifelong process.
Nurse-client relationship: A therapeutic relationship in which the nurse's goal is to help the client develop problem-solving coping mechanisms.
Mental health illness: Loss of the ability to respond to the environment (i.e., successfully adjust to changes) in accord with oneself and society.
Privacy and confidentiality: A client's reasonable expectation that information revealed to the nurse will not be disclosed to others. However, the nurse must explain to the client that information relevant to the individual's treatment plan must be shared with the other members of the treatment team, especially if the client has thoughts of harming himself or herself or others.

A female client who has just learned that she has breast cancer tells her family that the biopsy result was negative. What action should the nurse take?
A. Remind the client that the result was positive.
B. Ask the client to restate what the healthcare provider told her.
C. Talk to the family about the client's need for family support.
D. Encourage the client to talk to the nurse about her fears.

HESI Test Question Approach			
Positive?		YES	NO
Key Words			
Rephrase			
Rule Out Choices			
A	B	C	D

Coping and Defense Mechanisms
- Efforts to reduce anxiety
- Can be constructive or destructive
- *Coping* is related to problem solving.
- *Defense* is related to protecting oneself

Therapeutic Treatment Modalities

- *Milieu therapy:* The physical and social environment in which the client is receiving treatment
- *Interpersonal psychotherapy:* Use of a therapeutic relationship to modify the client's feelings, attitudes, and behaviors
- *Behavior therapy:* Can take many forms; used to change the client's behaviors
- *Cognitive therapy:* Directive, time-limited approach
- *Electroconvulsive therapy (ECT):* Electrically induced seizures, used for severely depressed individuals who do not respond to antidepressant medications and therapy

Group Therapy
- Involves a therapist and 5 to 8 members
- Provides feedback and support for the individual goals of each member
- Group therapy models
  — Psychoanalytic
  — Transactional analysis
  — Rogerian therapy
  — Gestalt therapy
- Interpersonal group therapy
- Self-help or support groups
- Family therapy
  — Family member with the presenting symptoms indicates the presence of problems in the entire family.
  — Change in one family member brings about changes in the others.

Stages of Group Development
- Initial stage: Superficial communication
- Working stage: Real work is done by group
- Termination stage: Provides group members with the opportunity to learn to deal with letting go

The PN and the mental health technician are assigned a group of mental health clients to lead in bingo, a social game activity. During the game, a male client begins to complain of shortness of breath and dizziness. Which intervention should the nurse provide first?
A. Send the client back to the unit.
B. Ask for a description of his feelings.
C. Escort the client to a quiet area.
D. Request an additional staff member.

HESI Test Question Approach			
Positive?		YES	NO
Key Words			
Rephrase			
Rule Out Choices			
A	B	C	D

Anxiety

- A normal, subjective experience that includes feelings of apprehension, uneasiness, uncertainty, or dread

Types of Anxiety
- Mild: Tension of everyday life
- Moderate: Immediate concerns
- Severe: A feeling that something bad is about to happen
- Panic: Terror and a sense of impending doom

Nursing Interventions
- Reduce stimuli in the environment
- Provide a calm, quiet environment
- May need to administer antianxiety agents

Anxiety Disorders
Generalized Anxiety Disorder
- Unrealistic anxiety about everyday worries
- Panic disorders produce a sudden feeling of intense apprehension

Posttraumatic Stress Disorder
- A re-experiencing of a traumatic event
- Recurrent and intrusive dreams or flashbacks
- Develops after an extremely traumatic event that involves injury or threat
- Individual feels intense helplessness, fear, and horror; traumatic event is relived repeatedly
- Treatment focuses on early recognition and emotionally supportive care

Phobia
- Irrational fear of an object, activity, or situation
- Client may recognize fear as unreasonable
- Associated with panic-level anxiety
- Defense mechanisms used include repression and displacement.

The nurse is planning to teach a male client strategies for coping with his anxiety. The nurse finds him in his room, compulsively washing his hands. What action should the nurse take next?
A. Teach the client alternatives as he washes his hands.
B. Ask him to stop his hand washing immediately.
C. Allow him to finish hand washing before teaching.
D. Ask what precipitated the hand washing.

Obsessive-Compulsive Disorder
- Obsessions—persistently intrusive thoughts
- Compulsions—repetitive behaviors designed to divert unacceptable thought and reduce anxiety

HESI Test Question Approach			
Positive?		YES	NO
Key Words			
Rephrase			
Rule Out Choices			
A	B	C	D

Antianxiety (Anxiolytic) Medications

- Depress the CNS; benzodiazepines have anxiety-reducing (anxiolytic), sedative-hypnotic, muscle relaxing, and anticonvulsant actions.
- Flumazenil (Romazicon), a benzodiazepine antagonist administered IV, reverses benzodiazepine intoxication in 5 minutes.

Somatoform Disorders

- Persistent worry or complaints regarding physical illness without physical findings
- Types of somatoform disorders
  — Conversion disorder
  — Hypochondriasis
  — Somatization disorders

The nurse is talking with a client who has a dissociative identity disorder, and the client begins to dissociate during the interaction. Which action should the nurse take?
A. Escort the client to art therapy group.
B. Call the client by name.
C. Talk about stressful feelings.
D. Move to another setting.

HESI Test Question Approach		
Positive?	YES	NO
Key Words		
Rephrase		
Rule Out Choices		
A	B	C	D

Dissociative Disorders

- Linked to exposure to a traumatic event
- Types of dissociative disorders
  — *Dissociative amnesia:* One or more episodes of inability to recall important personal information, usually of a traumatic nature
  — *Dissociative fugue:* Sudden, unexpected travel away from home, with inability to recall one's past
  — *Dissociative identity disorder:* Two or more distinct identities, at least two of which recurrently take control
  — *Depersonalization disorder:* Persistent or recurrent episodes of feelings of detachment from one's self

Personality Disorders

- Inflexible, maladaptive behavior patterns
- Client in touch with reality
- Lacks insight into his or her behavior
- Forms of acting out
  — Yelling and swearing
  — Cutting own skin
  — Manipulation
  — Substance abuse
  — Promiscuous sexual behavior
  — Suicide attempts

Clusters of Personality Disorders

Cluster A (Odd and Eccentric)
- Paranoid
- Schizoid
- Schizotypal

Cluster B (Emotional and Dramatic)
- Antisocial
- Borderline
- Histrionic
- Narcissistic

Cluster C (Anxious and Tense)
- Avoidant
- Dependent
- Obsessive-compulsive

Nursing and Collaborative Management
- Multiple psychotherapies are required to aid behavior change and promote satisfactory relationships
- Be alert to splitting, suicidal ideation
- Pharmacological intervention
  - Broad range; includes antianxiety agents, antidepressants; antipsychotic drugs

A female client who has borderline personality disorder returns after a weekend pass with lacerations to both wrists. The client vigorously complains to the nurse during the dressing change. The nurse's response should be:
A. Distant
B. Concerned
C. Matter of fact
D. Empathetic

HESI Test Question Approach			
Positive?		YES	NO
Key Words			
Rephrase			
Rule Out Choices			
A	B	C	D

Eating Disorders

Compulsive Overeating
- Bingelike overeating without purging
- Caused by lack of control over food consumption

Anorexia Nervosa
- Onset often associated with a stressful event.
- Client experiences altered body image.
- Death can occur from starvation, suicide, cardiomyopathies, or electrolyte imbalance.

Bulimia Nervosa
- Binge-purge syndrome
  - Eating binges followed by purging behaviors

A client with bulimia is admitted to the mental health unit. What intervention is most important for the PN to include in the initial treatment plan?
A. Observe the client after meals for vomiting.
B. Assess daily weight and vital signs.
C. Monitor serum potassium and calcium levels.
D. Provide a structured environment at mealtime.

<table>
<tr><td colspan="5">HESI Test Question Approach</td></tr>
<tr><td>Positive?</td><td></td><td></td><td>YES</td><td>NO</td></tr>
<tr><td>Key Words</td><td></td><td></td><td></td><td></td></tr>
<tr><td></td><td></td><td></td><td></td><td></td></tr>
<tr><td></td><td></td><td></td><td></td><td></td></tr>
<tr><td>Rephrase</td><td></td><td></td><td></td><td></td></tr>
<tr><td></td><td></td><td></td><td></td><td></td></tr>
<tr><td></td><td></td><td></td><td></td><td></td></tr>
<tr><td>Rule Out Choices</td><td></td><td></td><td></td><td></td></tr>
<tr><td>A</td><td>B</td><td>C</td><td>D</td><td></td></tr>
</table>

Mood Disorders

Depression
- Characterized by feelings of hopelessness and low self-esteem, as well as a tendency to take the blame for every negative event
- 25% of those with depression have suicidal ideation. Behavior therapy, cognitive behavioral therapy, and interpersonal psychotherapy all reduce symptoms of depression and maintain their effects well after treatment has ended

Suicide
- If the potential for suicide is suspected, the nurse should ask the client directly about thoughts of self-harm
  — Has the client felt the desire to harm himself or someone else?
  — Have any previous attempts been made to cause harm, and if so, what events surrounded the attempts?
  — What is the client's attitude about death?
  — What support systems are available to protect them from inflicting further harm?
- Treatment: The highest priority is to protect the client from inflicting harm, be vigilant, supervise medication administration, implement strategies to increase self-esteem and increase social support

Bipolar Disorders
- Characterized by episodes of mania and depression, between which client has periods of normal mood and activity
- Treatment: Lithium carbonate is the medication of choice; it can be toxic and requires regular monitoring of serum lithium levels
  — Other medications
    - Divalproex (Valproate)
    - Olanzapine (Zyprexa)
    - Carbamazepine (Tegretol)

Nursing and Collaborative Management
Selective Serotonin Reuptake Inhibitors (SSRIs)
- Inhibit serotonin reuptake

Tricyclic Antidepressants
- Block reuptake of norepinephrine (and serotonin) at presynaptic neuron
- May take 2 to 4 weeks after first dose to produce desired effect

Monoamine Oxidase Inhibitors (MAOIs)
- Inhibit the enzyme monoamine oxidase, which is present in the brain, blood platelets, liver, spleen, and kidneys.
- Used to treat clients with depression who have not responded to other antidepressant therapies, including electroconvulsive therapy.
- Concurrent use with amphetamines, antidepressants, dopamine, epinephrine, guanethidine, levodopa, methyldopa, nasal decongestants, norepinephrine, reserpine, tyramine-containing foods, or vasoconstrictors may cause hypertensive crisis.
- Concurrent use with opioid analgesics may cause hypertension or hypotension, coma, or seizures.

Schizophrenia

- Group of mental disorders characterized by psychotic features
  - Delusions of persecution: Client believes that he or she is being persecuted by some powerful force.
  - Delusions of grandeur: Client has an exaggerated sense of self that has no basis in reality.
  - Somatic delusions: Client believes that his or her body is changing, which has no basis in reality.

Perceptual Distortions
- Illusions: Brief experiences of misinterpretation or misperception of reality
- Hallucinations: May be auditory, visual, tactile, olfactory or gustatory with no basis in reality
- Safety is the priority
  - Make sure client does not have an auditory command telling him or her to harm self or others

Antipsychotic Medications
Traditional Medications
- Treat psychotic behavior
- Atypical Antipsychotics
  - Aripiprazole (Abilify)
  - Clozapine (Clozaril)
  - Olanzapine (Zyprexa)
  - Quetiapine (Seroquel)
  - Risperidone (Risperdal)
  - Ziprasidone (Geodon)
- Traditional Antipsychotics
  - Chlorpromazine (Thorazine)
  - Fluphenazine (Prolixin Decanoate)
  - Haloperidol

125

— Loxapine (Loxitane)
— Molindone hydrochloride (Moban)
— Pimozide (Orap)
— Thiothixene hydrochloride (Navane)

Side Effects
- Extrapyramidal
- Anticholinergic

Nursing Implications
- Encourage fluid (water)
- Gum
- Hard candy
- Increase fiber intake

Long-Acting Medications
- Promote medication compliance
- Risperidone (Risperdal Consta)
- Fluphenazine HCl (Prolixin)

Side Effects
- Blood dyscrasias
- Neuroleptic malignant syndrome

Nursing Implications
- Change client's position slowly for dizziness
- Report urinary retention to healthcare provider

Atypical Medications
- Treat all positive and negative symptoms

Side Effects
- Multiple side effects, depending on medication

Nursing Implications
- Tolerance to effects usually develops

Substance Abuse Disorders

Alcohol Abuse
- Alcohol is a central nervous system (CNS) depressant
  - *Physical dependence:* A biological need for alcohol to avoid physical withdrawal symptoms
  - *Psychological dependence:* A craving for the subjective effect of alcohol
  - *Intoxication:* A blood alcohol level of 0.1% (100 mg of alcohol per deciliter of blood) or greater

Disulfiram (Antabuse) Therapy
- Alcohol deterrent
- Instruct client to avoid using substances that contain alcohol (e.g., cough medicines, mouthwashes, after-shave lotions)

Other Medications That Assist with Cravings
- Acamprosate calcium (Campral)
- Naltrexone (ReVia)

Alcohol Withdrawal

- Signs peak after 24 to 48 hours.
- Chlordiazepoxide (Librium) is the most commonly prescribed medication for acute alcohol withdrawal.
- Withdrawal delirium peaks at 48 to 72 hours after cessation of intake and lasts 2 to 3 days.
  - **Medical emergency**
  - Death can occur from myocardial infarction, fat emboli, peripheral vascular collapse, electrolyte imbalance, aspiration pneumonia, or suicide.

A male client with a history of alcohol abuse is admitted to the medical unit for GI bleeding and pancreatitis. His admission data are: BP, 156/96 mmHg; pulse, 92 beats/min; temp, 99.2° F. Which intervention is most important for the nurse to provide?

A. Provide a quiet, low-stimulus environment.
B. Initiate seizure precautions.
C. Administer PRN lorazepam (Ativan) as prescribed.
D. Determine the time and amount of the client's last alcohol intake.

HESI Test Question Approach		
Positive?	YES	NO
Key Words		
Rephrase		
Rule Out Choices		
A	B	C	D

Cognitive Impairment Disorders

Autism

- Etiology unknown
- Clinical description
  - Hyperactivity
  - Short attention span
  - Impulsivity
  - Aggressivity
  - Self-injurious behaviors
  - Temper tantrums
  - Repetitive mannerisms
  - Preoccupation with objects
  - Spoken language often absent
  - "Islands of genius"
- *Prognosis:* There is no cure for autism. Language skills and intellectual level are the strongest factors related to the prognosis. Only a small percentage of individuals with the disorder go on to live and work independently as adults.

Asperger's Disorder

- A lifelong disorder with many features similar to those of autism; however, child does not show significant delays in language or cognitive development. The child may show impaired social and behavioral skills.

Attention Deficit/Hyperactivity Disorder (ADHD)

- Etiology: No known cause, but strong correlation between genetic factors and ADHD
- Clinical description
  - Fidgets when sitting
  - Gets up when expected to stay seated

— Excessive running when dangerous or inappropriate
— Loud, disruptive play during quiet activities
— Forgets and misses appointments
— Fails to meet deadlines
— Loses train of conversation
— Changes topics inappropriately
— Does not follow rules of games
- Treatment with CNS stimulants may be required to reduce hyperactive behavior and lengthen attention span.
- *Prognosis:* Disorder continues into adolescence in most children. Many adults who had been diagnosed with ADHD as children report a decrease in hyperactivity but continuing difficulty concentrating or attending to complex projects.

Dementia and Alzheimer's Disease

Dementia
- A syndrome of progressive deterioration in intellectual functioning secondary to structural or functional changes
- Marked by loss of long- and short-term memory
- Impairment in judgment, abstract thinking, problem-solving ability, and behavior

Alzheimer's Disease
- Irreversible form of senile dementia caused by nerve cell deterioration; most common type of dementia
- Priority in client care is providing a safe environment
- Maintain comfort; toilet as necessary; keep dry
- Reduce environmental stimulation during late afternoon and evening
- Maintain daily routine
- Provide environmental cues; turn on lights before dusk; provide night light
- Provide soothing music
- Provide reassurance and companionship, especially during difficult evening period

Medications
- Donepezil (Aricept)
- Galantamine (Razadyne)
- Memantine (Namenda)
- Rivastigmine (Exelon)
- Tacrine (Cognex)

A 71-year-old female client with Alzheimer's disease, who does not recognize her husband or children and forgets how to eat and dress, is admitted to the nursing home by the practical nurse. What is the PN's priority intervention for the newly admitted client?
A. Establish a daily routine and schedule.
B. Encourage involvement in structured activities.
C. Discuss strategies to coordinate care.
D. Stress the importance of self-nurturing.

HESI Test Question Approach		
Positive?	YES	NO
Key Words		
Rephrase		
Rule Out Choices		

A	B	C	D

Appendix A
Normal Laboratory Values

Test	Adult	Child	Infant/Newborn	Elder	Nursing Implications
Hematological					
Hgb (hemo-globin): g/dL	Male: 14-18 Female: 12-16 Pregnant: >11	1-6 yr: 9.5-14 6-18 yr: 10-15.5	Newborn: 14-24 0-2 wk: 12-20 2-6 mo: 10-17 6 mo–1 yr: 9.5-14	Values slightly decreased	High-altitude living increases values. Drug therapy can alter values. Slight Hgb decreases normally occur during pregnancy.
Hct (hemato-crit): %	Male: 42-52 Female: 37-47 Pregnant: >33	1-6 yr: 30-40 6-18 yr: 32-44	Newborn: 44-64 2-8 wk: 39-59 2-6 mo: 35-50 6 mo–1 yr: 29-43	Values slightly decreased	Prolonged stasis from vaso-constriction secondary to the tourniquet can alter values. Abnormalities in RBC size may alter Hct values.
RBC (red blood cell) count: 1 million/mm³	Male: 4.7-6.1 Female: 4.2-5.4	1-6 yr: 4-5.5 6-18 yr: 4.5-5	Newborn: 4.8-7.1 2-8 wk: 4-6 2-6 mo: 3.5-5.5 6 mo–1yr: 3.5-5.2	Same as adult	Never draw a specimen from an arm with an infusing IV. Exercise and high altitudes can cause an increase in values. Values are usually lower during pregnancy. Drug therapy can alter values.
WBC (white blood cell) count: 1,000/mm³	Both genders: 5-10	≤2 yr: 6.2-17 ≥2 yr: 5-10	Newborn, term: 9-30	Same as adult	Anesthetics, stress, exercise, and convulsions can cause increased values. Drug therapy can decrease values. 24-48 hr postpartum: A count as high as 25,000 is normal.
Platelet count: 1,000/mm³	Both genders: 150-400	150-400	Premature infant: 100-300 Newborn: 150-300 Infant: 200-475	Same as adult	Living at high altitudes, exercising strenuously, or taking oral contraceptives may increase values. Decreased values may be caused by hemorrhage, DIC, reduced production of platelets, infections, use of prosthetic heart valves, and drugs (e.g., acetaminophen, aspirin, chemotherapy, H_2 blockers, INH, Levaquin, streptomycin, sulfonamides, thiazide diuretics).

HESI Hint: The laboratory values that are most important to know for the NCLEX-RN exam are Hgb, Hct, WBCs, Na^+, K^+, BUN, blood glucose, ABGs (arterial blood gases), bilirubin for newborns, and therapeutic range for PT and PTT.

(Continued)

st	Adult	Child	Infant/Newborn	Elder	Nursing Implications
Hematological					
SED rate, ESR (erythrocyte sedimentation rate): mm/hr	Male: up to 15 Female: up to 20 Pregnant (all trimesters): up to 10	Same as adult	Newborn: 0-2	Same as adult	Rate is elevated during pregnancy.
PT (prothrombin time): sec	Both genders: 11-12.5 Pregnant: slight ↓	Same as adult	Same as adult	Same as adult	PT is used to help regulate Coumadin dosages. Therapeutic range: 1.5 to 2 times normal or control.
PTT (partial thromboplastin time): sec (see APTT, below)	Both genders: 60-70 Pregnant: slight ↓	Same as adult	Same as adult	Same as adult	PTT is used to help regulate heparin dosages. Therapeutic range: 1.5 to 2.5 times normal or control.
INR (international normalized ratio)	Both genders: 0.8-1.1	Same as adult	Same as adult	Same as adult	Ideal INR value must be individualized. Typical values for certain clients are: Clients with atrial fibrillation and DVT: between 2.0 and 3.0 Clients with mechanical heart valves: between 3.0 and 4.0.
APTT (activated partial thromboplastin time): sec	Both genders: 30-40	Same as adult	Same as adult	Same as adult	APTT is used to help regulate heparin dosages. Therapeutic range: 1.5 to 2.5 times normal or control.
Blood Chemistry					
Alkaline phosphatase: IU/L	Both genders: 30-120	2-8 yr: 65-210 9-15 yr: 60-300 16-21 yr: 30-200	<2 yr: 85-235	Slightly higher than adult	Hemolysis of specimen can cause falsely elevated values.
Albumin: g/dL	Both genders: 3.5-5 Pregnant: slight ↓	4.5-9	Premature infant: 3-4.2 Newborn: 3.5-5.4 Infant: 6-6.7	Same as adult	No special preparation is needed.
Bilirubin total: mg/dL	Total: 0.3-1 Indirect: 0.2-0.8 Direct: 0.1-0.3	Same as adult	Newborn: 1-12	Same as adult	Client is kept NPO, except for water, for 8-12 hr before testing. Prevent hemolysis of blood during venipuncture. Do *not* shake tube; this can cause inaccurate values. Protect blood sample from bright light.

(Continued)

Test	Adult	Child	Infant/Newborn	Elder	Nursing Implications
Hematological					
Calcium: mg/dL	Both genders: 9-10.5	8.8-10.8	<10 days: 7.6-10.4 Umbilical: 9-11.5 10 days–2 yr: 9-10.6	Values tend to decrease.	No special preparation is needed. Use of thiazide diuretics can cause increased calcium values.
Chloride: mEq/L	Both genders: 98-106	90-110	Newborn: 96-106 Premature infant: 95-110	Same as adult	Do not collect from an arm with an infusing IV solution.
Cholesterol: mg/dL	Both genders: <200	120-200	Infant: 70-175 Newborn: 53-135	Same as adult	Do not collect from an arm with an infusing IV solution.
CPK (creatine phosphokinase): IU/L	Male: 55-170 Female: 30-135	Same as adult	Newborn: 65-580	Same as adult	Specimen must not be stored before running test.
Creatinine: mg/dL	Male: 0.6-1.2 Female: 0.5-1.1	Child: 0.3-0.7 Adolescent: 0.5-1	Newborn: 0.2-0.4 Infant: 0.3-1.2	Decrease in muscle mass may cause decreased values.	NPO for 8 hr before testing is preferred but not required. BUN-to-creatinine ratio of 20:1 indicates adequate kidney functioning.
Glucose: mg/dL	Both genders: 70-110	≤2 yr: 60-100 >2 yr: 7	Cord: 45-96 Premature infant: 20-60 Newborn: 30-60 Infant: 40-90	Normal range increases after age 50.	Client is kept NPO, except for water, for 8 hr before testing. Stress, infection, and caffeine can cause increased values.
HCO_3^-: mEq/L	Both genders: 23-30	20-28	Newborn: 13-22 Infant: 20-28	Same as adult	None
Iron: mcg/dL	Male: 80-180 Female: 60-160	50-120	Newborn: 100-250	Same as adult	NPO for 8 hr before test is preferred but not required.
TIBC (total iron binding capacity): mcg/dL	Both genders: 250-460	Same as adult	Same as adult	Same as adult	None
LDH (lactic dehydrogenase): IU/L	Both genders: 100-190	60-170	Newborn: 160-450 Infant: 100-250	Same as adult	Do not give IM injections for 8-12 hr before test. Hemolysis of blood causes a false positive result.
Potassium: mEq/L	Both genders: 3.5-5	3.4-4.7	Newborn: 3-5.9 Infant: 4.1-5.3	Same as adult	Hemolysis of specimen can result in falsely elevated values. Exercise of the forearm with tourniquet in place may cause an increased potassium level.
Protein total: g/dL	Both genders: 6.4-8.3	6.2-8	Premature infant: 4.2-7.6 Newborn: 4.6-7.4 Infant: 6-6.7	Same as adult	NPO for 8 hr before test is preferred but not required.

(Continued)

Test	Adult	Child	Infant/Newborn	Elder	Nursing Implications
Hematological					
AST/SGOT (aspartate aminotransferase): IU/L	0-35 Female slightly lower than adult male	3-6 yr: 15-50 6-12 yr: 10-50 12-18 yr: 10-40	0-5 days: 35-140 <3 yr: 15-60	Slightly higher than adult	Hemolysis of specimen can result in falsely elevated values. Exercise may cause an increased value.
ALT/SGPT (alanine aminotransferase): IU/mL	Both genders: 4-36	Same as adult	Infants' values may be twice as high as those of adults.	Slightly higher than adult	Hemolysis of specimen can result in falsely elevated values. Exercise may cause an increased value.
Sodium: mEq/L	Both genders: 136-145	136-145	Newborn: 134-144 Infant: 134-150	Same as adult	Do not collect from an arm with an infusing IV solution.
Triglycerides: mg/dL	Male: 40-160 Female: 35-135	6-11 yr: 31-108 12-15 yr: 36-138 16-19 yr: 40-163	0-5 yr: 30-86	Same as adult	Client is kept NPO for 12 hr before test. No alcohol for 24 hr before test.
BUN (blood urea nitrogen): mg/dL	Both genders: 10-20	5-18	Newborn: 3-12 Cord: 21-40 Infant: 5-18	Slightly higher	None
Arterial Blood Chemistry					
pH	Both genders: 7.35-7.45	Same as adult	Newborn: 3-12 Cord: 21-40 Infant: 5-18	Same as adult	Specimen must be heparinized. Specimen must be iced for transport. All air bubbles must be expelled from sample. Direct pressure to puncture site must be maintained.
P_{CO_2}: mmHg	Both genders: 35-45	Same as adult	<2 yr: 26-41	Same as adult	Specimen must be heparinized. Specimen must be iced for transport. All air bubbles must be expelled from sample. Direct pressure to puncture site must be maintained.
P_{O_2}: mmHg	Both genders: 80-100	Same as adult	Newborn: 60-70	Same as adult	Specimen must be heparinized. Specimen must be iced for transport. All air bubbles must be expelled from sample. Direct pressure to puncture site must be maintained.

(Continued)

Test	Adult	Child	Infant/Newborn	Elder	Nursing Implications
			Hematological		
Hco_3^-: mEq/L	Both genders: 21-28	Same as adult	Infant/newborn: 16-24	Same as adult	Specimen must be heparinized. Specimen must be iced for transport. All air bubbles must be expelled from sample. Direct pressure to puncture site must be maintained.
O_2 Saturation: %	Both genders: 95-100	Same as adult	Newborn: 40-90	95	Specimen must be heparinized. Specimen must be iced for transport. All air bubbles must be expelled from sample. Direct pressure to puncture site must be maintained.

From Pagana TJ, Pagana KD: *Mosby's manual of diagnostic and laboratory test reference,* ed 4, St Louis, 2010, Mosby.

BUN, Blood urea nitrogen; *DIC,* disseminated intravascular coagulation; *DVT,* deep vein thrombosis; *IM,* intramuscular; *INH,* isoniazid; *NPO,* nothing by mouth; *Pco₂,* carbon dioxide partial pressure; *Po₂,* oxygen partial pressure; *Hco₃⁻,* bicarbonate.

Appendix B
Comparison of Three Types of Hepatitis

Characteristics	Hepatitis A (Infectious Hepatitis)	Hepatitis B (Serum Hepatitis)	Hepatitis C
Source of infection	• Contaminated food • Contaminated water or shellfish	• Contaminated blood products • Contaminated needles or surgical instruments • Mother to child at birth	• Contaminated blood products • Contaminated needles, IV drug use • Dialysis
Route of infection	• Oral • Fecal • Parenteral • Person to person	• Parenteral • Oral • Fecal • Direct contact • Breast milk • Sexual contact	• Parenteral • Sexual contact
Incubation period	15-50 days	14-180 days	14-180 days (average)
Onset	Abrupt	Insidious	Insidious
Seasonal variation	• Autumn • Winter	All year	All year
Age group affected	• Children • Young adults	Any age	Any age
Vaccine	Yes	Yes	No
Inoculation	Yes	Yes	Yes
Potential for chronic liver disease	No	Yes	Yes
Immunity	Yes	Yes	No
Treatment	• Prevention—Hepatitis A (HAV) vaccine • Proper hand washing • Avoid contaminated food or water • Obtain immunoglobulin within 14 days if exposed to the virus	• Prevention—Hepatitis B (HBV) vaccine for high-risk groups • Antiviral and immunomodulating drugs	• Subcutaneous pegylated interferon alpha once a week and oral ribavirin (Copegus, Rebetol) daily
Complications	Very few	• Chronic hepatitis • Cirrhosis • Hepatitis D • Liver cancer	• Chronic hepatitis • Cirrhosis • Liver cancer

NCLEX-PN Examination Practice Questions

Management

1. Which activity should the practical nurse (PN) delegate to unlicensed assistive personnel (UAP)? (Select all that apply.)
   A. Observe a client with cirrhosis to see whether he can hear any better after discontinuation (DC) of an IV antibiotic
   B. Encourage additional oral fluids to an elderly client with pneumonia who develops a fever
   C. Report the ability of a client with myasthenia gravis to eat the meal on the supper tray unassisted
   D. Record the number of liquid stools of a client who has received lactulose
   E. Take the vital signs of clients scheduled for early morning tests

HESI Test Question Approach		
Positive?	**YES**	**NO**
Key Words		
Rephrase		
Rule Out Choices		
A	B	C	D

2. The PN is delegating several client tasks to the UAP. Which client requires an intervention by the PN?
   A. The client with active TB who is leaving his room without a mask
   B. The client with pneumonia and dehydration who has not had anything to drink for 4 hours
   C. The client with asthma who complains of being anxious and unable to concentrate
   D. The client with COPD who is leaving the unit to smoke, even though his next IVPB is due

HESI Test Question Approach		
Positive?	**YES**	**NO**
Key Words		
Rephrase		
Rule Out Choices		
A	B	C	D

3. The PN reports that a hospitalized client has threatened to cut herself. Which priority nursing intervention should the PN implement?
   A. Schedule an extra nurse for the next shift
   B. Immediately assign a UAP to sit with the client
   C. Ask that the charge nurse move the client to another room with a roommate
   D. Continue to establish rapport and ensure confidentiality

HESI Test Question Approach		
Positive?	**YES**	**NO**
Key Words		
Rephrase		
Rule Out Choices		
A	B	C	D

4. The UAP is assisting with the care of eight clients on a postpartum unit. Which assignment should the PN delegate to the UAP?
   A. Assess fundal firmness and lochia for the clients who delivered vaginally
   B. Take vital signs every 15 minutes for a client with preeclampsia
   C. Provide breast-feeding instructions for a primigravida
   D. Assist with daily care activities for the clients on bed rest

HESI Test Question Approach		
Positive?	YES	NO
Key Words		
Rephrase		
Rule Out Choices		
A	B	C	D

Advanced Clinical Concepts

5. Which client is at the highest risk for developing respiratory complications?
   A. A 21-year-old with dehydration and cerebral palsy who is dependent in daily activities
   B. A 60-year-old who has had type 2 diabetes for 20 years who was admitted with cellulitis
   C. An obese 30-year-old with hypertension who is noncompliant with the medication regimen
   D. A 40-year-old with a serum K^+ of 3.4 mEq/L who is taking a loop diuretic and who complains of fatigue

HESI Test Question Approach		
Positive?	YES	NO
Key Words		
Rephrase		
Rule Out Choices		
A	B	C	D

6. A PN stops at an accident and finds a young adult lying next to an overturned truck. The victim is pulseless and apneic, and his skin smells of gasoline. Which action has the highest priority?
   A. Initiate basic life support
   B. Remove the victim's clothing
   C. Assess for hemorrhage
   D. Remove glass shards from the victim's face

HESI Test Question Approach		
Positive?	YES	NO
Key Words		
Rephrase		
Rule Out Choices		
A	B	C	D

7. A postoperative client has received normal saline intravenously at 125 mL/hr. The PN observes a dark yellow urine output. The first hour the output was 50 mL; the next hour, it was 32 mL; and the third hour, it was 28 mL. What action should the PN take?
   A. Give a bolus with $D_5\frac{1}{2}$ NS at 200 mL/hr
   B. Inform the healthcare provider
   C. Monitor output for another 2 hours
   D. Draw samples for the BUN and creatinine labs

HESI Test Question Approach			
Positive?		YES	NO
Key Words			
Rephrase			
Rule Out Choices			
A	B	C	D

8. Which finding(s) would indicate a positive outcome for administration of fresh frozen plasma (FFP) to a client with liver disease? (Select all that apply.)
   A. Normal BUN and creatinine level
   B. Hemoglobin level of 10 gm/dL
   C. Return to normal temperature
   D. Decreased bleeding from gums
   E. Negative guaiac for occult blood

HESI Test Question Approach			
Positive?		YES	NO
Key Words			
Rephrase			
Rule Out Choices			
A	B	C	D

9. A client's arterial blood gas results are: pH, 7.29; P_{CO_2}, 55; and HCO_3, 26. Which is the correct interpretation of these values?
   A. Normal blood gas values
   B. Respiratory acidosis
   C. Respiratory alkalosis
   D. Metabolic acidosis

HESI Test Question Approach			
Positive?		YES	NO
Key Words			
Rephrase			
Rule Out Choices			
A	B	C	D

10. A client who has chronic back pain is not receiving adequate pain relief from an oral analgesic. Which alternative action should the PN explore to promote the client's independence?
   A. Ask the healthcare provider to increase the analgesic dosage
   B. Obtain a prescription for a second analgesic, to be administered by the IV route
   C. Consider the client's receptivity to complementary therapy
   D. Encourage counseling to prevent future addiction

HESI Test Question Approach		
Positive?	YES	NO
Key Words		
Rephrase		
Rule Out Choices		
A	B	C	D

Maternal-Newborn Nursing

11. A client at 41-weeks' gestation who is in active labor calls the PN to report that her membranes have ruptured. The PN views the perineum and sees the cord. What is the PN's highest priority action that should be implemented?
   A. Place the client in a knee-chest position
   B. Cover the cord with sterile, warm, NS gauze
   C. Assist with preparing for an emergency cesarean birth
   D. Start O_2 by face mask at 10 L/min

HESI Test Question Approach		
Positive?	YES	NO
Key Words		
Rephrase		
Rule Out Choices		
A	B	C	D

12. A client at 39 weeks' gestation plans to have an epidural block when labor is established. What intervention(s) should the PN implement to prevent side effects? (Select all that apply.)
   A. Reinforce teaching about the effects of the epidural
   B. Place the client in a chair next to the bed with her feet elevated
   C. Administer a bolus of 500 mL of normal saline solution
   D. Monitor the fetal heart rate and contractions continuously
   E. Assist the client to empty her bladder every 2 hours

HESI Test Question Approach		
Positive?	YES	NO
Key Words		
Rephrase		
Rule Out Choices		
A	B	C	D

13. A client whose last menses was 6 weeks ago presents in the clinic with RLQ abdominal pain, no vaginal bleeding, and pain in her right shoulder. Which action should the PN take first?
    A. Check for abdominal rebound tenderness, distention, and fever
    B. Obtain vital signs, assist with IV access, and observe for shock
    C. Observe for recent musculoskeletal injury, bruising, or abuse
    D. Collect specimens for a pregnancy test, hemoglobin, and WBC

HESI Test Question Approach			
Positive?		YES	NO
Key Words			
Rephrase			
Rule Out Choices			
A	B	C	D

14. A pregnant client with a low hematocrit and low hemoglobin asks the PN why she should take her iron supplement. Which explanation should the PN offer?
    A. Iron promotes collagen production, which aids healing during the postpartum period
    B. Iron reduces the risk of preterm labor
    C. Replacing iron through the diet alone is difficult
    D. Additional iron is necessary to replace the blood lost during delivery

HESI Test Question Approach			
Positive?		YES	NO
Key Words			
Rephrase			
Rule Out Choices			
A	B	C	D

Medical-Surgical Review

15. A client is returning to the unit after an intravenous pyelogram (IVP). Which intervention should the PN include in the plan of care?
    A. Maintain bed rest
    B. Increase fluid intake
    C. Monitor for hematuria
    D. Continue NPO status

HESI Test Question Approach			
Positive?		YES	NO
Key Words			
Rephrase			
Rule Out Choices			
A	B	C	D

16. The PN's client has chronic urinary tract infections. The PN is reinforcing teaching to the client about a prescription for ciprofloxacin (Cipro) 500 mg PO bid. What side effect(s) could the client expect over the course of medication therapy? (Select all that apply.)
    A. Photosensitivity
    B. Dyspepsia
    C. Diarrhea
    D. Urinary frequency
    E. Pernicious anemia

HESI Test Question Approach			
Positive?		YES	NO
Key Words			
Rephrase			
Rule Out Choices			
A	B	C	D

17. Several of the PN's clients are complaining of pain. To which client should the PN respond first?
    A. The client who has bladder pain while receiving a continuous saline irrigant 2 hours after a transurethral prostatic resection
    B. The client with incisional pain on the third day post nephrectomy who requests a PRN oral pain medication
    C. The client with flank pain that is partially relieved by passage of a renal calculus
    D. The client with bladder spasms after drainage of 1,000 mL of urine during insertion of an indwelling catheter

HESI Test Question Approach			
Positive?		YES	NO
Key Words			
Rephrase			
Rule Out Choices			
A	B	C	D

18. A client with a Tenckhoff catheter calls the clinic to report that he feels poorly and seems to have a fever. What is the PN's best response?
    A. Encourage the client to come to the clinic today to be evaluated
    B. Instruct the client to increase his fluid intake to 3 L/day
    C. Review the client's medication regimen for adherence
    D. Ask about the client's recent dietary intake of protein and iron

HESI Test Question Approach			
Positive?		YES	NO
Key Words			
Rephrase			
Rule Out Choices			
A	B	C	D

19. A client is admitted with chest pain. Which finding(s) support the admitting problem and should be reported to the charge nurse? (Select all that apply.)
A. Elevated ST segment
B. Crisp S_1 S_2
C. Elevated troponin level
D. Radiating jaw pain
E. O_2 saturation of 93%

HESI Test Question Approach			
Positive?		**YES**	**NO**
Key Words			
Rephrase			
Rule Out Choices			
A	**B**	**C**	**D**

20. The PN is reviewing the discharge instructions with a client who has a history of angina. Which instruction should the PN emphasize as the most important?
A. Avoid activity that requires the Valsalva maneuver
B. Seek emergency treatment if chest pain persists after the third nitroglycerin dose
C. Rest for 30 minutes after having chest pain before resuming activity
D. Keep extra nitroglycerin in an airtight, light-resistant bottle

HESI Test Question Approach			
Positive?		**YES**	**NO**
Key Words			
Rephrase			
Rule Out Choices			
A	**B**	**C**	**D**

21. The PN is reviewing the medication diltiazem (Cardizem) with a client who is preparing to go home. Which dietary recommendation has the highest priority?
A. Maintain a low-sodium diet
B. Eat a banana each morning
C. Eat high-fiber foods daily
D. Avoid grapefruit products

HESI Test Question Approach			
Positive?		**YES**	**NO**
Key Words			
Rephrase			
Rule Out Choices			
A	**B**	**C**	**D**

22. A female client with a history of Raynaud's disease is preparing for discharge and wants to know how to manage her symptoms. What teaching should the PN reinforce?
A. Take oral analgesic at regularly spaced intervals
B. Avoid extremes of heat and cold
C. Limit foods and fluids with caffeine
D. Keep involved extremities in a dependent position

HESI Test Question Approach			
Positive?		YES	NO
Key Words			
Rephrase			
Rule Out Choices			
A	B	C	D

23. The PN is providing care for a client admitted with thrombocytopenia. Which problem should the PN immediately report to the charge nurse?
A. Bleeding gums
B. Refusing breakfast
C. Complains of insomnia
D. Constant fatigue

HESI Test Question Approach			
Positive?		YES	NO
Key Words			
Rephrase			
Rule Out Choices			
A	B	C	D

24. A client who is admitted with cancer of the larynx is scheduled for a laryngectomy tomorrow. What client education should the PN review with him tonight?
A. Body image counseling
B. Pain management expectations
C. Communication techniques
D. Postoperative nutritional needs

HESI Test Question Approach			
Positive?		YES	NO
Key Words			
Rephrase			
Rule Out Choices			
A	B	C	D

25. A victim of a motor vehicle collision is dead on arrival at the emergency department. Which action should the nurse take to assist the spouse with this crisis?
   A. Ask whether there are relatives, friends, or clergy to call
   B. Talk about the former relationship with the spouse
   C. Provide education about the stages of grief and loss
   D. Assess the spouse's level of anxiety

HESI Test Question Approach

Positive?		YES	NO
Key Words			
Rephrase			
Rule Out Choices			
A	B	C	D

26. The PN is interviewing a client in the prenatal clinic for violence during pregnancy. Which statement(s) would describe an appropriate technique for assessing for violence? (Select all that apply.)
   A. Women should be assessed only if they are members of a high-risk group
   B. Women may be assessed in the presence of young children
   C. Women should be assessed once during pregnancy
   D. Women should be reassessed face to face by a nurse as the pregnancy progresses
   E. Women should be assessed alone (i.e., without the intimate partner)

HESI Test Question Approach

Positive?		YES	NO
Key Words			
Rephrase			
Rule Out Choices			
A	B	C	D

27. The PN reminds several clients on the mental health unit that breakfast is at 8 AM, medications are given at 9 AM, and group therapy sessions begin at 10 AM. Which treatment modality has been implemented?
   A. Milieu therapy
   B. Behavior modification
   C. Peer therapy
   D. Problem solving

HESI Test Question Approach

Positive?		YES	NO
Key Words			
Rephrase			
Rule Out Choices			
A	B	C	D

28. The PN is taking a client to the x-ray department. As the nurse starts to enter the elevator with him, the client becomes panic-stricken and states, "I can't do this." Which intervention should the PN implement first?
   A. Ask one more staff member to ride in the elevator
   B. Offer an antianxiety medication
   C. Begin desensitization about riding the elevator
   D. Affirm his fears about riding the elevator

HESI Test Question Approach

Positive?		YES	NO
Key Words			
Rephrase			
Rule Out Choices			
A	B	C	D

29. A male client who experiences frequent nightmares is found one night trying to strangle his roommate. Which action intervention is the PN's highest priority?
   A. Giving the client a sedative
   B. Asking the victim to share his feelings
   C. Moving the client to a private room
   D. Talking with both clients about the event

HESI Test Question Approach

Positive?		YES	NO
Key Words			
Rephrase			
Rule Out Choices			
A	B	C	D

30. The PN is providing care for a client with a borderline personality disorder who is being manipulative. Which intervention should be included?
   A. Refer the client's requests to one nurse
   B. Avoid challenging inappropriate behavior
   C. Limit the client's contact with other clients
   D. Remove consequences for acting-out behaviors

HESI Test Question Approach

Positive?		YES	NO
Key Words			
Rephrase			
Rule Out Choices			
A	B	C	D

31. An adolescent client, admitted to the mental health unit for anorexia nervosa, frequently isolates herself. What is the PN's priority intervention?
    A. Teach the client about the importance of self-expression
    B. Monitor the client's activities while she is awake
    C. Include the client in daily group therapy
    D. Facilitate social interactions with others

HESI Test Question Approach			
Positive?		**YES**	**NO**
Key Words			
Rephrase			
Rule Out Choices			
A	B	C	D

32. The PN is planning the daily schedule for clients on the mental health unit. A client who is manic should be encouraged to participate in which group activity?
    A. A basketball game in the gym
    B. Jogging at least 1 mile
    C. A Ping-Pong game with a peer
    D. Group with the art therapist

HESI Test Question Approach			
Positive?		**YES**	**NO**
Key Words			
Rephrase			
Rule Out Choices			
A	B	C	D

Delegation and Prioritization

33. A PN is making client assignments for the night shift. The nursing team has another PN and two UAPs. Which duties could be delegated to the UAPs? (Select all that apply.)
    A. Transport a client who has had a stroke to the radiology department for a chest radiograph
    B. Reinforce the technique for insulin injection to a client newly diagnosed with diabetes
    C. Bathe a 25-year-old client with sickle cell disease who has multiple IV lines and a PCA pump
    D. Turn a 92-year-old client with end-stage heart failure who has a DNR order
    E. Inform family members in clients' rooms that visiting hours are over

HESI Test Question Approach			
Positive?		**YES**	**NO**
Key Words			
Rephrase			
Rule Out Choices			
A	B	C	D

34. A hospitalized client has type 2 diabetes. Which task(s) for this client can the PN delegate to the UAP? (Select all that apply.)
A. Contacting the dietitian for a prescribed consult
B. Reporting the client's insulin injection technique
C. Obtaining the fingerstick blood glucose level before meals
D. Reminding the client to dry the toes carefully after a shower
E. Talking with the client about foods that raise the blood glucose level

HESI Test Question Approach			
Positive?		**YES**	**NO**
Key Words			
Rephrase			
Rule Out Choices			
A	**B**	**C**	**D**

35. After a change of shift report, the PN reviews her assignments. Which client should the PN assess first?
A. An elderly client receiving palliative care for heart failure who complains of constipation and nervousness
B. An adult client who is 48 hours postoperative from a colectomy who reports nausea
C. A middle-aged client with chronic renal failure whose urinary catheter has drained 95 mL over 8 hours
D. A client taking Coumadin who is receiving oxygen at 3 L/min and whose respiratory rate is 12 breaths/min

HESI Test Question Approach			
Positive?		**YES**	**NO**
Key Words			
Rephrase			
Rule Out Choices			
A	**B**	**C**	**D**

36. The PN in the clinic suspects that a 78-year-old client is being abused. What assessment finding(s) would support this? (Select all that apply.)
A. Client's unexplained crying while the PN talks
B. Client states, "My son is stealing my jewelry."
C. Area of thinning hair on the scalp
D. Disheveled appearance
E. Symmetrical bruises on the legs

HESI Test Question Approach			
Positive?		**YES**	**NO**
Key Words			
Rephrase			
Rule Out Choices			
A	**B**	**C**	**D**

37. The PN enters the exam room after a client has been told by her healthcare provider that she has advanced ovarian cancer. Which response by the nurse is likely to be most supportive of the client?
   A. "I know many women who have survived ovarian cancer."
   B. "Let's talk about the treatments for ovarian cancer."
   C. "In my opinion, getting a second opinion would be a good idea."
   D. "Tell me about what you're feeling right now."

HESI Test Question Approach

Positive?			YES	NO
Key Words				
Rephrase				
Rule Out Choices				
A	B		C	D

38. Which assessment finding indicates the expected outcome of administering donepezil (Aricept) to a client with Alzheimer's disease?
   A. Increased muscle strength and tone
   B. Fewer episodes of urinary incontinence
   C. Increased ability to solve simple problems
   D. Improve appetite, which supports weight gain

HESI Test Question Approach

Positive?			YES	NO
Key Words				
Rephrase				
Rule Out Choices				
A	B		C	D

39. In caring for an older client with dementia who has sundowning syndrome, which intervention(s) should the PN implement? (Select all that apply.)
   A. Observe for tiredness at the end of the day
   B. Maintain a quiet unit during the late afternoon
   C. Monitor for medication side effects
   D. Assess for decreased gross motor movement
   E. Reorient the client to reality

HESI Test Question Approach

Positive?			YES	NO
Key Words				
Rephrase				
Rule Out Choices				
A	B		C	D

40. The PN starts to help an elderly client with dementia get out of bed. The client becomes angry and yells at the nurse, "Get out of here! I'll get up when I'm ready." Which response by the nurse is most likely to be helpful in reducing the client's agitation?
    A. "Your healthcare provider has prescribed daily ambulation for you."
    B. "You must ambulate to prevent complications that are very serious."
    C. "I know how you feel; you're angry about having to do this, but it's required."
    D. "I'll be back in 30 minutes to help you get out of bed and walk around the room."

HESI Test Question Approach

Positive?		YES	NO
Key Words			
Rephrase			
Rule Out Choices			
A	B	C	D

41. The PN administers NPH insulin 15 units subcutaneously to a client before the evening meal (5:30 PM). During which interval should the nurse be alert for signs or symptoms of a hypoglycemic reaction?
    A. 6:30 PM to 8:30 PM
    B. 11:30 PM to 1:30 AM
    C. 3:30 AM to 5:30 AM
    D. 7:30 AM to 9:30 AM

HESI Test Question Approach

Positive?		YES	NO
Key Words			
Rephrase			
Rule Out Choices			
A	B	C	D

Answers and Rationales

Management

1. **Which activity should the practical nurse (PN) delegate to unlicensed assistive personnel (UAP)? (Select all that apply.)**

Rationales:

A. *Observe a client with cirrhosis to see whether he or she can hear any better after discontinuation (DC) of an IV antibiotic*
This requires assessment about ototoxicity, which is beyond the scope of the UAP.

B. *Encourage additional oral fluids to an elderly client with pneumonia who develops a fever*
These directions are not sufficiently clear and detailed for the UAP to perform the task.

C. *Report the ability of a client with myasthenia gravis to eat the meal on the supper tray unassisted*
This requires assessment of the client's clinical status that is beyond the scope of the UAP.

D. *Record the number of liquid stools of a client who has received lactulose*
This is a task that encompasses basic care, elimination, and intake and output; it does not require judgment or the expertise of the nurse. It can be performed by the UAP.

E. *Take the vital signs of clients scheduled for early morning tests*
This is a task that can easily be performed by the UAP and does not require interpretation of data.

2. **The PN is delegating several client tasks to the UAP. Which client requires an intervention by the PN?**

Rationales:

A. *The client with active TB who is leaving his room without a mask*
A UAP can be delegated to provide a box of masks or to direct the client back to his room.

B. *The client with pneumonia and dehydration who has not had anything to drink for 4 hours*
A UAP can be directed to provide specific types and amounts of fluids.

C. *The client with asthma who complains of being anxious and unable to concentrate*
This client is at risk for airway compromise and requires assessment. The PN should respond to this client.

D. *The client with COPD who is leaving the unit to smoke, even though his next IVPB is due*
The UAP can ask the client to delay leaving the unit.

3. **The PN reports that a hospitalized client has threatened to cut herself. Which priority nursing intervention should the PN implement?**

Rationales:

A. *Schedule an extra nurse for the next shift*
The charge nurse should plan ahead for staffing, but the immediate focus should be on the client's safety.

B. *Immediately assign a UAP to sit with the client*
Because the client is at risk for suicide, a staff member should stay with the client.

C. *Ask that the charge nurse move the client to another room with a roommate*
This will not ensure the client's safety, and a staff member should be present with the client at all times

D. *Continue to establish rapport and ensure confidentiality*
Building rapport is important, but this client is a suicide risk; building rapport at this time and ensuring confidentiality will not ensure the client's safety, which is the priority.

4. **The UAP is assisting with the care of eight clients on a postpartum unit. Which assignment should the PN delegate to the UAP?**

Rationales:

A. *Assess fundal firmness and lochia for the clients who delivered vaginally*
Assessment is one of the roles of the nurse and is not consistent with the role of the UAP.

B. *Take vital signs every 15 minutes for a client with preeclampsia*
This is a high-risk client who needs to be evaluated by a licensed nurse.

C. *Provide breast-feeding instructions for a primigravida*
Teaching is also the responsibility of a licensed nurse.

D. *Assist with daily care activities for the client on bed rest*
This is the most appropriate assignment for the UAP. The PN should delegate daily care activities to the UAP on the basis of the client's needs.

Advanced Clinical Concepts

5. **Which client is at the highest risk for developing respiratory complications?**

Rationales:

A. *A 21-year-old with dehydration and cerebral palsy who is dependent in daily activities*
A client with dehydration and cerebral palsy (characterized by uncoordinated and spastic muscle movements that can cause ADL dependence) is at an increased risk for respiratory problems because of impaired mobility and swallowing.

B. A 60-year-old who has had type 2 diabetes for 20 years who was admitted with cellulitis
This client is more at risk for renal, cardiac, and/or vascular complications.

C. An obese 30-year-old with hypertension who is non-compliant with the medication regimen
An obese individual who is noncompliant with antihypertensive meds is more at risk for cardiac or cerebral events than respiratory problems.

D. A 40-year-old with a serum K⁺ of 3.4 mEq/L who is taking a loop diuretic and who complains of fatigue
This middle-aged adult is hypokalemic and fatigued but is not at high risk for respiratory problems.

6. **A PN stops at an accident and finds a young adult lying next to an overturned truck. The victim is pulseless and apneic, and his skin smells of gasoline. Which action has the highest priority?**

Rationales:

A. *Initiate basic life support*
Initiating CPR is vital to this victim's survival; it is the first priority.

B. **Remove the victim's clothing**
The top priority is to institute CPR.

C. **Assess for hemorrhage**
Accident victims are at risk for internal or external hemorrhage; however, this assessment does not have the highest priority.

D. **Remove glass shards from the victim's face**
Other life-threatening situations require action before the removal of glass.

7. **A postoperative client has received normal saline intravenously at 125 mL/hr. The PN observes a dark yellow urine output. The first hour the output was 50 mL; the next hour, it was 32 mL; and the third hour, it was 28 mL. What action should the PN take?**

Rationales:

A. *Give a bolus of D_5 ½ NS at 200 mL/hr*
This is not a recommended action, because hypertonic solutions are prescribed for fluid and electrolyte imbalances and cause an osmotic movement of fluids into the vasculature.

B. *Inform the healthcare provider*
Low urinary output may be a serious problem and requires more immediate intervention

C. **Monitor output for another 2 hours**
Urine output has been monitored and may indicate dehydration, which can lead to more serious complications.

D. **Draw samples for BUN and creatinine labs**
BUN and creatinine should be evaluated, but this is not the immediate priority.

8. **Which finding(s) would indicate a positive outcome for administration of fresh frozen plasma (FFP) to a client with liver disease? (Select all that apply.)**

Rationales:

A. **Normal BUN and creatinine levels**
Although BUN and creatinine are important to review, these values are not affected by administration of FFP.

B. **Hemoglobin level of 10 gm/dL**
FFP does not affect hemoglobin levels.

C. **Return to normal temperature**
Although monitoring the client's temperature is important, FFP does not have a direct effect on this value.

D. *Decreased bleeding from gums*
FFP replaces clotting factors; therefore, detecting any occult (hidden) or obvious bleeding provides valuable information about the client's status.

E. *Negative guaiac for occult blood*
FFP replaces clotting factors; therefore, detecting any occult (hidden) or obvious bleeding provides valuable information about the client's status.

9. **A client's arterial blood gas results are: pH–7.29, P_{CO_2}–55, and H_{CO_3}–26. Which is the correct interpretation of these values?**

Rationales:

A. **Normal blood gas values**
Normal arterial blood gas values are: pH–7.35-7.45; P_{CO_2}–35-45; and H_{CO_3}–22-26.

B. *Respiratory acidosis*
The client's P_{CO_2} is 55, which demonstrates CO_2 retention and hypoventilation. The pH of 7.29 reflects acidosis with no compensation, therefore, is respiratory acidosis.

C. **Respiratory alkalosis**
Typically ABG values indicating respiratory alkalosis are: pH–7.48, P_{CO_2}–33, and H_{CO_3}–23.

D. **Metabolic acidosis**
ABG values indicating metabolic acidosis are: pH–7.30, P_{CO_2}–40, and H_{CO_3}–20.

10. **A client who has chronic back pain is not receiving adequate pain relief from an oral analgesic. What alternative action should the PN explore to promote the client's independence?**

Rationales:

A. **Ask the healthcare provider to increase the analgesic dosage**
Although this intervention may improve pain relief, it may not promote self-care without increasing side effects that may affect the client's independence.

B. Obtain a prescription for a second analgesic, to be administered by the IV route

The IV route does not promote self-care and may cause additional side effects that interfere with the client's independence in ADLs.

C. _Consider the client's receptivity to complementary therapy_

This action supports increased pain control and self-care without the level of adverse effects associated with additional medication. It is the least invasive measure and promotes the active participation (self-care) of the client.

D. Encourage counseling to prevent future addiction

Referrals may be necessary; however, it is the PN's responsibility to intervene with measures to manage pain and maintain self-care.

Maternal-Newborn Nursing

11. A client at 41 weeks' gestation who is in active labor calls the PN to report that her membranes have ruptured. The PN views the perineum and sees the cord. What is the PN's highest priority action that should be implemented?

Rationales:

A. _Place the client in a knee-chest position_

This is the most critical intervention to prevent cord compression by the presenting part, which would impair fetal oxygenation and lead to both morbidity and mortality.

B. Cover the cord with sterile, warm, NS gauze

If the cord is protruding outside the vagina, this should be done to prevent drying of the Wharton jelly; however, it is not the priority intervention.

C. Assist with preparing for an emergency cesarean birth

This should be done by the staff while the client is kept in position to maintain the presenting part of the cord.

D. Start O₂ by face mask at 10 L/min

Oxygen should be provided to the mother to increase oxygen to the fetus via the placenta; however, the priority is to maintain the presenting part of the cord.

12. A client at 39-weeks' gestation plans to have an epidural block when labor is established. What intervention(s) should the PN implement to prevent side effects? (Select all that apply.)

Rationales:

A. Reinforce teaching about the effects of the epidural

Teaching the client about the procedure and the expected results of epidural analgesia is an important nursing intervention; however, it does not prevent the side effect of hypotension related to the initial epidural medication.

B. Place the client in a chair next to the bed with her feet elevated

An epidural block reduces lower extremity sensation and movement to varying degrees. Positions such as sitting in a chair may not be possible during epidural pain management; also, they may be a safety risk and may not prevent side effects.

C. _Administer a bolus of 500 mL of normal saline solution_

Prehydration will increase maternal blood volume and prevent hypotension, which occurs as a result of vasodilation, a side effect of epidural anesthesia. A saline solution is used to prevent fetal secretion of insulin that later places the neonate at risk for hypoglycemia.

D. Monitor the fetal heart rate and contractions continuously

Vital signs should be monitored every 5 minutes immediately after the initial epidural dose, and if stable, then every 15 minutes.

E. _Assist the client to empty her bladder every 2 hours_

Because the client may be unable to determine whether she has a full bladder, assisting her to void every 2 hours prevents urinary retention, a side effect of epidural anesthesia.

13. A client whose last menses was 6 weeks ago presents in the clinic with RLQ abdominal pain, no vaginal bleeding, and pain in her right shoulder. Which action should the PN take first?

Rationales:

A. Check for abdominal rebound tenderness, distention, and fever

Bleeding related to an ectopic pregnancy may present these manifestations, but first the PN should assess for hypovolemic shock.

B. _Obtain vital signs, assist with IV access, and observe for shock_

The PN should first evaluate the client's vital signs for indications of shock related to a ruptured ectopic pregnancy (an obstetric emergency). A vascular access is vital if shock should occur.

C. Observe for recent musculoskeletal injury, bruising, or abuse

This may be part of the assessment if a life-threatening situation is ruled out first.

D. Collect specimens for a pregnancy test, hemoglobin level, and WBC

A pregnancy test should be done and CBC specimens should be collected, but first the PN should continue to monitor the client for manifestations of intraabdominal bleeding (e.g., referred shoulder pain related to blood collection under the diaphragm).

14. **A pregnant client with a low hematocrit and low hemoglobin asks the PN why she should take her iron supplement. Which explanation should the PN offer?**

Rationales:

A. *Iron promotes collagen production, which aids healing during the postpartum period*
This does not explain the need for the additional iron.

B. *Iron reduces the risk of preterm labor*
This does not explain the need for the additional iron.

C. <u>*Replacing iron through the diet alone is difficult*</u>
With the expansion of plasma volume and the use of iron by the fetus to build hemoglobin, pregnant women have difficulty replacing iron losses through nutrition alone.

D. *Additional iron is necessary to replace blood loss during delivery*
This does not explain the need for the additional iron.

Medical-Surgical Review

15. **A client is returning to the unit after an intravenous pyelogram (IVP). Which intervention should the PN include in the plan of care?**

Rationales:

A. *Maintain bed rest*
There is no need to restrict mobility after an IVP.

B. <u>*Increase fluid intake*</u>
The client should increase PO fluids to facilitate excretion of the dye, thereby preventing possible side effects.

C. *Monitor for hematuria*
There is no risk of hematuria from an IVP.

D. *Continue NPO status*
The client should resume fluid intake after an IVP to facilitate excretion of the dye.

16. **The PN's client has chronic urinary tract infections. The PN is reinforcing teaching to the client about a prescription for ciprofloxacin (Cipro) 500 mg PO bid. What side effect(s) could the client expect over the course of medication therapy? (Select all that apply.)**

Rationales:

A. <u>*Photosensitivity*</u>
This is a side effect of Cipro; exposure to sunlight or tanning beds should be avoided. The client should be instructed to use sunscreen and to wear protective clothing.

B. <u>*Dyspepsia*</u>
Cipro causes GI irritation, nausea and vomiting, and abdominal pain, which should be reported.

C. <u>*Diarrhea*</u>
Watery, foul-smelling diarrhea is an adverse reaction to Cipro that is an indicator of pseudomembranous

colitis; this must be reported and requires immediate intervention.

D. *Urinary frequency*
Although not a side effect of Cipro, urinary frequency may indicate that the medication is ineffective and should be reported.

E. *Pernicious anemia*
This is not an expected side effect of Cipro.

17. **Several of the PN's clients are complaining of pain. To which client should the PN respond first?**

Rationales:

A. <u>*The client who has bladder pain while receiving a continuous saline irrigant 2 hours after a transurethral prostatic resection*</u>
This client is at risk of clot formation occluding the catheter, which may indicate bleeding and bladder distention. The nurse should evaluate this client immediately.

B. *The client with incisional pain on the third day post nephrectomy who requests a PRN oral pain medication*
This client is not as high a priority as the client in option A, because the client is not at risk of altered homeostasis.

C. *The client with flank pain that is partially relieved by passage of a renal calculus*
This client's condition is not likely to worsen, because the stone was passed. This client should be evaluated after the client in option A.

D. *The client with bladder spasms after drainage of 1,000 mL of urine during insertion of an indwelling catheter*
This client's pain, which reflects bladder spasms, is of a lower priority than the pain of the client in option A.

18. **A client with a Tenckhoff catheter calls the clinic to report that he feels poorly and seems to have a fever. What is the PN's best response?**

Rationales:

A. <u>*Encourage the client to come to the clinic today to be evaluated*</u>
Tenckhoff catheters are used in peritoneal dialysis. The catheter places the client at risk for peritoneal infection. Because clients receiving peritoneal dialysis usually have some degree of immune compromise and anemia, this client should come to the clinic to be assessed.

B. *Instruct the client to increase his fluid intake to 3 L/day*
Clients who need dialysis retain fluid and usually are restricted to an intake that is only 300 mL greater than output.

C. Review the client's medication regimen for adherence

The nurse should evaluate the client's adherence; however, assessing the client for infection is a higher priority.

D. Ask about the client's recent dietary intake of protein and iron

Iron deficiency and protein loss are common problems in clients who are receiving peritoneal dialysis. Although monitoring dietary intake is important, it does not take priority over evaluating for possible infection.

19. A client is admitted with chest pain. Which finding(s) support the admitting problem and should be reported to the charge nurse? (Select all that apply.)

Rationales:

A. *Elevated ST segment*

ECG findings that indicate MI include ST-segment elevation and the development of Q waves.

B. *Crisp S_1S_2*

This is a normal assessment finding.

C. *Elevated troponin level*

Troponin I is cardiac specific and therefore a highly specific indicator of an MI.

D. *Radiating jaw pain*

Pain is the foremost symptom of MI, and jaw pain is classic.

E. *O_2 saturation of 93%*

This is a normal finding.

20. The PN is reviewing the discharge instructions with a client who has a history of angina. Which instruction should the PN emphasize as the most important?

Rationales:

A. *Avoid activity that requires the Valsalva maneuver*

Although minimizing or avoiding the Valsalva maneuver decreases anginal pain, it is not the most important issue.

B. *Seek emergency treatment if chest pain persists after the third nitroglycerin dose*

This instruction is the most important, because chest pain characteristic of acute MI persists longer than 15 minutes, and delaying medical treatment can be life threatening.

C. *Rest for 30 minutes after having chest pain before resuming activity*

Waiting 30 minutes may be recommended only if the nitroglycerin is effective.

D. *Keep extra nitroglycerin in an airtight, light-resistant bottle*

This is an excellent medication teaching point; however, it does not have the same urgency as seeking emergency care.

21. The PN is reviewing the medication diltiazem (Cardizem) with a client who is preparing to go home. Which dietary recommendation has the highest priority?

Rationales:

A. *Maintain a low-sodium diet*

The client may need to restrict the sodium intake, but that is not specific for Cardizem.

B. *Eat a banana each morning*

If the client has low potassium, this should be recommended; however, it is not the highest priority.

C. *Eat high-fiber foods daily*

This is an excellent teaching point for everyone, but it is not specific for Cardizem.

D. *Avoid grapefruit products*

Grapefruit should be avoided by clients taking calcium channel blockers, because it can cause an increase in the medication's serum level, predisposing the client to hypotension.

22. A female client with a history of Raynaud's disease is preparing for discharge and wants to know how to manage her symptoms. What teaching should the PN reinforce?

Rationales:

A. *Take oral analgesic at regularly spaced intervals*

Pain, unlike the feeling of cold hands and fingers, is not always associated with Raynaud's syndrome. If pain is present, it is sporadic and situational, which should not require continuous medication.

B. *Avoid extremes of heat and cold*

In Raynaud's syndrome, vascular spasms of the hands and fingers are triggered by extremes of heat or cold. The PN should encourage the client to avoid these triggers, which elicit pallor and cold-to-the-touch sensations.

C. *Limit foods and fluids with caffeine*

Caffeine is not a primary trigger, but it should be limited if the client notes that it contributes to blanching.

D. *Keep involved extremities in a dependent position*

This is not effective for a client with Raynaud's syndrome.

23. The PN is providing care for a client admitted with thrombocytopenia. Which problem should the PN immediately report to the charge nurse?

Rationales:

A. *Bleeding gums*

Bleeding gums are considered a sign of thrombocytopenia (low platelet count) and should be reported.

B. *Refusing breakfast*

Although a poor appetite may be a symptom of thrombocytopenia, reporting bleeding gums takes priority in the client with thrombocytopenia.

C. Complains of insomnia
Insomnia is not a typical symptom associated with thrombocytopenia and is not the priority problem at this time.

D. Constant fatigue
This is a problem typically associated with a client who is anemic.

24. A client who is admitted with cancer of the larynx is scheduled for a laryngectomy tomorrow. What client education should the PN review with him tonight?

Rationales:

A. Body image counseling
This is a common need after the diagnosis has been made, surgery has been performed, and basic needs and communication techniques have been met.

B. Pain management expectations
Pain management is important, but the ability to vocalize or convey these needs should be addressed first.

C. Communication techniques
The nurse should review communication techniques, making sure the client understands alternative ways to express and convey basic subjective needs in the immediate postoperative period.

D. Postoperative nutritional needs
Nutrition is important to promote healing, but the client should understand ways to communicate needs in the immediate postoperative period.

Psychiatric Nursing

25. A victim of a motor vehicle collision is dead on arrival at the emergency department. Which action should the nurse take to assist the spouse with this crisis?

Rationales:

A. Ask whether there are relatives, friends, or clergy to call
The PN should help the spouse identify support systems and resources for coping.

B. Talk about the former relationship with the spouse
The PN should focus on immediate needs for coping and support; the spouse may be unable to process information during the crisis.

C. Provide education about the stages of grief and loss
The spouse is unable to focus on learning about grief and loss during the crisis.

D. Assess the spouse's level of anxiety
Although the level of anxiety affects the client's response to the crisis, the PN should assist the client in coping with the present stressful event.

26. The PN is interviewing a client in the prenatal clinic about violence during pregnancy. Which statement(s) would describe an appropriate technique for assessing for violence? (Select all that apply.)

Rationales:

A. Women should be assessed only if they are members of a high-risk group.
Violence against women occurs in all ethnic groups and at all income levels.

B. Women may be assessed in the presence of young children.
It is important that children not be present, because they may repeat what is heard. Infants may be present.

C. Women should be assessed only once during pregnancy.
Many women do not reveal violence the first time they are asked. As trust develops between nurse and client, the client may be more comfortable sharing her story. Also, violence may start later in the pregnancy.

D. Women should be reassessed face to face by a nurse as the pregnancy progresses.
Having more than one face-to-face interview elicits the highest reports of violence during pregnancy.

E. Women should be assessed alone, without the intimate partner.
Interviewing the client in private allows her to be comfortable in sharing her story

27. The PN reminds several clients on the mental health unit that breakfast is at 8 AM, medications are given at 9 AM, and group therapy sessions begin at 10 AM. Which treatment modality has been implemented?

Rationales:

A. Milieu therapy
Milieu therapy uses resources and activities in the environment to assist with improving social functioning and activities of daily living.

B. Behavior modification
Behavior modification involves changing behaviors with positive and negative reinforcements to allow desired activities or remove privileges.

C. Peer therapy
Peer therapy is not a single therapeutic modality, but peers are responsible for supporting, sharing, and compromising within their peer group and milieu.

D. Problem solving
Problem solving is related to crisis intervention where the nurse focuses on the problem and ways to reestablish previous levels of functioning.

28. The PN is taking a client to the radiography department. As the nurse starts to enter the elevator, the client becomes panic-stricken and states, "I can't do this." Which intervention should the PN implement first?

Rationales:

A. *Ask one more staff member to ride in the elevator*
One more staff member will not be able to assist the client to overcome his fears until he first can recognize his feelings.

B. *Offer an antianxiety medication*
Offering an antianxiety medication may be necessary to begin desensitization but is not the priority.

C. *Begin desensitization about riding the elevator*
Desensitizing the client may be implemented, but first the client should identify his fear and recognize his anxiety.

D. *Affirm his fears about riding the elevator*
The PN should first affirm the client's feelings of anxiety and fear about riding the elevator; then options for desensitization may be considered.

29. A male client who experiences frequent nightmares is found one night trying to strangle his roommate. Which intervention is the PN's highest priority?

Rationales:

A. *Giving the client a sedative*
A sedative may reduce anxiety and encourage sleep, but safety is the most important intervention.

B. *Asking the victim to share his feelings*
Processing the trauma with the victim is important, but safety is the priority.

C. *Moving the client to a different room*
The PN should focus on safety as the immediate concern and move the client to a private room to protect both clients from harm.

D. *Talking with both clients about the event*
Although both clients should talk about the incident, this is not an opportune time. The PN should separate the clients as a safety precaution.

30. The PN is providing care for a client with a borderline personality disorder who is being manipulative. Which intervention should be included?

Rationales:

A. *Refer the client's requests to one nurse*
The best intervention is to provide consistency and avoid splitting by assigning the client to only one nurse.

B. *Avoid challenging inappropriate behavior*
The PN should assist the client to recognize manipulative behavior and set limits on manipulative behaviors as needed.

C. *Limit the client's contacts with other clients*
Socialization should be encouraged to improve skills with others.

D. *Remove consequences for acting-out behavior*
Firm limits with clear expectations and consequences are necessary for clients who are manipulative.

31. An adolescent client, admitted to the mental health unit for anorexia nervosa, frequently isolates herself. What is the PN's priority intervention?

Rationales:

A. *Teach the client about the importance of self-expression*
Self-expression of feelings is important, but re-establishing eating habits is the priority intervention.

B. *Monitor the client's activities while she is awake*
The PN should monitor and supervise the client's activities to prevent bingeing, purging, or avoiding meals.

C. *Include the client in daily group therapy*
The client should be included in daily groups, but the priority is her physiological needs, including monitoring meals.

D. *Facilitate social interactions with others*
The client should be given opportunities to socialize, but monitoring activities during the day, especially meals, is the priority.

32. The PN is planning the daily schedule for clients on the mental health unit. A male client who is manic should be encouraged to participate in which group activity?

Rationales:

A. *A basketball game in the gym*
The client should avoid any potentially competitive physical activity; basketball is a contact sport that may stimulate aggressive acting-out behavior.

B. *Jogging at least 1 mile*
Jogging is the best activity for this client, because it is a noncompetitive physical activity that expends the energy associated with mania.

C. *A Ping-Pong game with a peer*
The PN should avoid assigning the client to competitive activities that can cause frustration and stimulate mood swings.

D. Group with the art therapist
A manic client may become disruptive and distracted in an art group; also, physical energy using large muscle groups is more effective for expending energy.

Delegation and Prioritization

33. A PN is making client assignments for the night shift. The nursing team has another PN and two UAPs. Which duties could be delegated to the UAPs? (Select all that apply.)

Rationales:

A. *Transport a client who has had a stroke to the radiology department for a chest radiograph*
UAPs may obtain vital signs and weight and height measurements, perform care activities, transport clients, and do secretarial work. The PN should instruct the UAP in the proper precautions for these delegated procedures as needed.

B. **Reinforce the technique for injecting insulin to a client newly diagnosed with diabetes**
The ability to reinforce teaching requires the critical thinking and knowledge application skills unique to the licensed nurse.

C. *Bathe a 25-year-old client with sickle cell disease who has multiple IV lines and a PCA pump*
The UAP may obtain vital signs, weight and height measurements, perform care activities, and secretarial work. Instruct UAP on proper precautions for these delegated procedures as needed

D. *Turn a 92 year old client with end stage heart failure who has a DNR order*
UAPs may obtain vital signs and weight and height measurements, perform care activities, transport clients, and do secretarial work. The PN should instruct the UAP in the proper precautions for these delegated procedures as needed.

E. *Inform family members in client's rooms that visiting hours are over*
UAPs may obtain vital signs and weight and height measurements, perform care activities, transport clients, and do secretarial work. The PN should instruct the UAP in the proper precautions for these delegated procedures as needed.

34. A hospitalized client has type 2 diabetes. Which task(s) for this client can the PN delegate to the UAP? (Select all that apply.)

Rationales:

A. *Contacting the dietitian for a prescribed consult*
The UAP may perform simple secretarial tasks.

B. **Reporting the client's insulin injection technique.**
The ability to reinforce teaching requires the critical thinking and knowledge application skills unique to the licensed nurse.

C. *Obtaining the fingerstick blood glucose level before meals*
The UAP may obtain fingerstick blood glucose levels.

D. *Reminding the client to dry the toes carefully after a shower*
Hygiene tasks may be delegated to the UAP.

E. **Talking with the client about foods that raise the blood glucose level**
The ability to reinforce teaching requires the critical thinking and knowledge application skills unique to the licensed nurse.

35. After a change of shift report, the PN reviews her assignments. Which client should the PN assess first?

Rationales:

A. **An elderly client receiving palliative care for heart failure who complains of constipation and nervousness**
Constipation and nervousness are concerns, but these are common problems in palliative care; this is not the priority client.

B. *An adult client who is 48 hours postoperative from a colectomy who reports nausea*
Postoperative nausea (PON) is a common reaction after surgery and a particular concern after abdominal surgery. PON can stress and irritate abdominal and GI wounds, causing further complications.

C. **A middle-aged client with chronic renal failure whose urinary catheter has been draining 95 mL for over 8 hours**
Oliguria or anuria is an expected outcome in chronic renal failure; this is not the priority client.

D. **A client taking Coumadin who is receiving oxygen at 3 L/min and whose respiratory rate is 12 breaths/min**
A respiratory rate of 12 breaths/min is an acceptable vital sign; this is not the priority client.

36. The PN in the clinic suspects that a 78-year-old client is being abused. Which assessment finding(s) would support this? (Select all that apply.)

Rationales:

A. *Unexplained client's crying while the PN talks*
This may indicate elder abuse.

B. *The client states, "My son is stealing my jewelry."*
This may indicate elder abuse.

C. **An area of thinning hair on the scalp**
Thinning hair in elderly men and women is part of the aging process.

D. *Disheveled appearance*
This may indicate elder abuse.

E. *Symmetrical bruises on the legs*
This may indicate elder abuse.

37. The PN enters the exam room after a client has been told by her healthcare provider that she has advanced ovarian cancer. Which response by the nurse is likely to be most supportive for the client?

Rationales:

A. *"I know many women who have survived ovarian cancer."*
Providing an opinion does not allow the client to process her feelings.

B. *"Let's talk about the treatments for ovarian cancer."*
Providing facts does not allow the client to process her feelings.

C. *"In my opinion, getting a second opinion would be a good idea."*
Providing an opinion does not allow the client to process her feelings.

D. *"Tell me about what you're feeling right now."*
This statement allows the client to decide on the communication; if the PN is directing and talking, the goals of therapeutic communication are thwarted.

38. Which assessment finding indicates the expected outcome of administering donepezil (Aricept) to a client with Alzheimer's disease?

Rationales:

A. *Increased muscle strength and tone*
Aricept does not improve muscle strength.

B. *Fewer episodes of urinary incontinence*
Aricept does not improve continence.

C. *Increased ability to solve simple problems*
Aricept is used for mild to moderate Alzheimer's disease and helps improve cognitive function.

D. *Improved appetite, supporting weight gain*
Aricept does not improve appetite.

39. In caring for an older client with dementia who has sundowning syndrome, which intervention(s) should the PN implement? (Select all that apply.)

Rationales:

A. *Observe for tiredness at the end of the day*
Monitoring the client for tiredness is important, because these signs may affect sundowning syndrome.

B. *Maintain a quiet unit during the late afternoon*
Noise levels can affect the client's orientation level. A noisy environment may increase agitation as the day progresses.

C. *Monitor for medication side effects*
Monitoring the client for side effects is important, because these may affect sundowning syndrome.

D. *Assess for decreased gross motor movement*
This is not an expected finding with sundown syndrome

E. *Reorient the client to reality*
Reality orientation does not work in the client with dementia and often increases agitation.

40. The PN begins to assist an elderly client with dementia to get out of bed. The client becomes angry and yells at the nurse, "Get out of here! I'll get up when I'm ready." Which response by the nurse is most likely to be helpful in reducing the client's agitation?

Rationales:

A. *"Your healthcare provider has prescribed daily ambulation for you."*
Providing information to a client who cannot process his or her behavior only increases the client's agitation.

B. *"You must ambulate to prevent complications that are very serious."*
Providing information to a client who cannot process his or her behavior only increases the client's agitation.

C. *"I know how you feel; you're angry about having to do this, but it is required."*
Providing information to a client who cannot process his or her behavior only increases the client's agitation.

D. *"I'll be back in 30 minutes to help you get out of bed and walk around the room."*
Clients with dementia are unable to reflect on their unacceptable behavior and learn to control it. Therefore, providing a "time out" away from the nurse is the correct response. The client needs the time and space to de-escalate.

41. The PN administers NPH insulin 15 units subcutaneously to a client before the evening meal (5:30 PM). During what interval should the nurse be particularly alert for signs or symptoms of a hypoglycemic reaction?

Rationales:

A. *6:30 PM to 8:30 PM*
This is not an anticipated hypoglycemic interval for NPH, an intermediate-acting insulin.

B. *11:30 PM to 1:30 AM*
With NPH, the risk for a hypoglycemic reaction peaks 6 to 8 hours after injection.

C. *3:30 AM to 5:30 AM*
This is not an anticipated hypoglycemic interval for NPH, an intermediate-acting insulin.

D. *7:30 AM to 9:30 AM*
This is not an anticipated hypoglycemic interval for NPH, an intermediate-acting insulin.